Well Done, Beef Wellington

Max Davidson

CORONET BOOKS
Hodder and Stoughton

For my parliamentary friends
Down Under, g'day and thank you

The characters and situations in this book are entirely imaginary and bear no relation to any real person or actual happenings.

The right of Max Davidson to be identified as the author of this work has been asserted by him in accordance with the Copyright, Designs and Patents Act 1988.

Printed and bound in Great Britain for Hodder and Stoughton Paperbacks, a division of Hodder and Stoughton Ltd., Mill Road, Dunton Green, Sevenoaks, Kent TN13 2YA. (Editorial Office: 47 Bedford Square, London WC1B 3DP) by Clays Ltd, St Ives plc. Photoset by Rowland Phototypesetting Ltd., Bury St Edmunds, Suffolk.

A CIP catalogue record for this title is available from the British Library

ISBN 0-340-56460-1

CONTENTS

WELL DONE, BEEF WELLINGTON

'I don't want semantics, Beef, I want facts. Are these two jokers having it off or aren't they?'

'Of course they are. I've seen them at it.'

'Where?'

'In the National Gallery.'

'That place on Trafalgar Square? What, kissing? Holding hands?'

'Of course not. They're not stupid. They were looking at a painting of the Crucifixion. By some dead Iti.'

'So how . . . ?'

I fixed him with a stern look. 'Chief, this is madness. Use your common sense. Would *you* go to the National Gallery with a woman if you weren't bonking her?'

'You know I wouldn't. This Hockley-Giles character, how old is he?'

'Sixty-eight. He's retiring at the next election.'

'And the girl?'

'Thirty, thirty-five. First parliament. Goes in for leather jackets and single earrings.'

'Kinky.'

'The whole thing's kinky. It will keep politics off the front page for weeks. What about it, Chief?'

About the author

Max Davidson was born in 1955 and published his first novel, *The Wolf*, in 1983. Beef Wellington, his roly-poly tabloid lobby correspondent, first saw the light of day two years later, in *Beef Wellington Blue*. Davidson's other successes include *Hugger Mugger*, *Suddenly in Rome* and *The Greek Interpreter*. He also reviews fiction regularly for the *Daily* and *Sunday Telegraph*.

I

COCK HORROR PROBE

Don't get me wrong about this. I love the House of Commons.

I love its antiquity. I love its grubbiness. I love it when it's being solemn. I love it when it's teetering on the edge of farce. I love the shouting and the jokes and the points of order and the quaint old rigmaroles. I love the lobbies and the corridors and the bars. Especially the bars.

Most of all I love the people. The honourables and the right honourables and the honourable-and-learneds and the honourable-and-gallants and the honourable-and-mads and the honourable-and-tight-as-owls. The new boys, with their dreams and their hopes and their voices which haven't broken properly. The rising stars. The has-beens and the nearly-has-beens and the never-weres. The old lags, with their gout and their cynicism. And the women, with their smart clothes and their tired faces and their heels clicking across the flagstones in the Members Lobby. The biggest shower you'll ever see and the best men and women in the world. I love the lot of them.

I wouldn't work anywhere else if you paid me. But there are days when the place gets me down a bit. Days when I think I'd be better off tending six sheep and a goat on a Welsh hillside.

Days like the day I appeared before the select committee last year.

What happened was this. I, John Joseph Wellington, known to the world as Beef Wellington on account of my stupendous girth, am a lobby correspondent. If you're not familiar with the term, lobby correspondents are a sub-species of journalists who hang around the House of Commons getting the inside gen on the big political stories of the day. On a paper like mine, which starts with six pages of sex, ends with six pages of sport and puts politics under the bingo on page seven, the duties are inevitably light. If the Prime Minister drops dead at the dispatch-box with a knife between his shoulder-blades, I report the fact in a few well-chosen words and it may make page two. Otherwise I sit around the bars with my ears open and fade into the background. Nice work if you can get it.

The thing about this sort of life, apart from its effect on the waistline, is that it depletes the morale but liberates the imagination. Outwardly you adopt a world-weary air as if you've seen it all before, but the romantic dreamer inside works overtime. You don't see the world straight – and that's how I got caught. I picked up the scent of a scandal involving a Cabinet Minister, a beautiful Dutch woman and a dead body by the roadside and I let the whole thing go to my head. The Minister was as bent as a corkscrew but not, as I had surmised, a murderer; and even on a paper like mine, it pays to get that sort of detail right. The name of Beef Wellington has never been synonymous with responsible journalism and I hope never will be, but this was my darkest hour. When a Select Committee on Press Ethics was set up eighteen months later, I was pretty much in the firing line.

The scenes in the Press Bar when this committee was announced were unforgettable. Bob Mumford nearly fell off his stool. White Walker let out a guffaw which could be heard in the House of Lords. Big Mac rocked to and fro like a man having a heart seizure. The rest of us just howled till the tears ran down our cheeks. It was the best joke we'd heard since the one about the Chief Whip and the Spanish ambassador.

The committee started taking evidence from interested bodies and soon my number came up. I couldn't see that I was an interested body as the whole exercise left me cold; but at twenty-two stone in my boxer shorts I certainly have an interesting body, so presumably there had been a typing mistake. Be that as it may, I was summoned before the committee with two of my fellow lobby correspondents: Bob Mumford and Tom 'Tiger' Hancock.

Bob writes an immensely serious column for one of those Sunday extravaganzas which weigh about five and a half pounds and have done so much to spoil the thinking man's weekend. Tiger's the political correspondent for one of the middle-brow dailies. I represented the tabloid interest. If it had been a trade union conference, of course, I could have wielded ten million votes to their 300,000. But Parliament doesn't work like that. The other two were expected to do most of the talking, while I kept mum and looked pale and interesting.

You've probably seen one of these select committees on television. Their members sit around in a horseshoe firing questions at some poor sods who are supposed to know all the answers. In tone, a cross between *Mastermind* and *Blankety Blank*.

Bob and Tiger were handling the questions easily enough and a sort of post-prandial lethargy had enveloped the proceedings when Alan Price, the committee chairman, turned to me.

'I wonder if Mr Wellington has a view on that?'

My attention had wandered, frankly, and I was caught off-guard. The safest answer seemed to be a non-committal grunt.

'Could you repeat that please, Mr Wellington?'

I delivered a second grunt. Louder, more statesmanlike but still non-committal.

'I'm sorry, Mr Wellington, I'm going to have to ask you to speak up for the benefit of our shorthand writer. Do you basically agree with what your colleagues have just said?'

'To, uh, some extent, yes.'

'In what respect do you disagree with them? This is all most interesting.'

'In respect that – different people see things differently. Mr Mumford is his own man. Mr Hancock is his own man. I'm my own man. At the same time, we're all journalists and that means, I suppose – we all write for newspapers.'

I paused for breath and noticed the members of the committee looking at me keenly, as if I was an elderly relative who might shortly need to be put in a home.

Inspiration finally came. 'I'm sure, Chairman,' I said smoothly, 'I don't need to labour the point. Your committee have wide experience of these matters and will understand my position perfectly.'

The chairman smiled and a purr of pleasure passed round the table. It's always the way with politicians: roll them over on their backs and tickle them and they'll let you get away with murder. I was off the hook.

'Can you remind me, Mr Wellington,' asked one of the other Members, 'what paper you write for?'

This was more my level of question. I gave the name of my organ and I gave it with pride.

'And what is its circulation?'

'About three million. With a readership of half a million.'

'I don't quite follow the point you're making, Mr Wellington.'

'The other two and a half million buy it for the pictures.'

I beamed, to indicate that this was satire. There was a frosty silence broken by a rasping cough from the chairman.

'Could you confine yourself to the facts please, Mr Wellington?'

'Very well, Chairman.'

'This is a proceeding of Parliament.'

'Quite understood, Chairman.'

'We're not in the entertainment business.'

'No indeed, Chairman.'

A woman Member continued the questioning and served up another slow long-hop outside the leg-stump.

'What would you describe as a journalist's main function, Mr Wellington?'

'To sell newspapers.'

'You don't think you have any wider responsibilities?'

'Wider?' I scratched my ear. 'Such as?'

'Such as providing accurate information and educating the public.'

'I thought that's what schools were for.'

I beamed again. No good. It was like doing a Thursday matinée in Cheltenham.

'And how far do you think it's legitimate to go to sell newspapers?' asked another Member. A petulant little man answering to the name of Glazebury. 'Would you, for example, ever fabricate or embellish a story?'

I looked at him in amazement. The idea that a paper like mine would print a story which *hadn't* been fabricated or embellished belonged with the goblins and the pixies.

'I would add colour as necessary,' I said diplomatically.

'Even at the expense of the truth?'

I wanted to say 'Particularly at the expense of the truth', but restrained myself. There are times when manly frankness wins friends and times when it doesn't.

'The truth,' I said, 'is a movable feast. Facts which might seem relevant to, say, Mr Mumford here would not interest me and vice versa. I like to think I give my readers a version of the truth.'

'But not the whole truth?'

'A version of the whole truth.'

'And what about personal privacy?' he barked. 'How far do you feel justified in investigating people's private lives in order to establish your version of what you call the truth?'

I surveyed him coldly. He had a carrying voice and was in danger of giving these previously friendly exchanges the flavour of a midnight visit by the Gestapo. I decided to answer fire with fire.

'NUJ guidelines are quite specific on that point, Mr Glazebury. People's private lives are their own affair, unless they make a damn good read, in which case they become public property. Does that answer your question?'

'Perfectly,' he said, with a sinister glint in his eye. 'Perfectly.'

The session concluded with the chairman bowling me an easy one about what I would do if a leaked document came into my possession containing sensitive information about the security services.

'Publish and be damned!' I cried, to thunderous applause from the public gallery.

'Bob,' I said after the meeting, as we held a boozy post-mortem in the Press Bar, 'was I imagining things or did Glazebury's behaviour strike you as rather odd?'

'No odder than usual.'

'What I'm getting at is this. He asked that question about privacy, I blew the proverbial raspberry and, instead of getting hot under the collar as I expected, he just retired to his corner with a wicked grin on his face like a stooge in a pantomime. What's the matter with the man? I didn't expect him to agree with me, but he might have argued back.'

'What's the point, Beef? You'd made his case for him. You're on record as saying that it's all right to intrude on someone's privacy so long as you get a good story out of it.'

'Well, isn't it?'

'Of course it is. But we'd never actually admit to that on my paper. It sounds bad.'

I pondered this. 'On my paper we'd never admit to anything else. We've got our standards. So what are you saying, Bob? That I've confirmed Glazebury's prejudices?'

'Exactly. He'll quote what you said and try to persuade the committee to make some tough recommendations for shackling the press.'

'The Government won't take any notice. It throws select committee reports straight in the bin.'

'This time may be different. The Government would

never dare take on the press on its own, but if it was backed by an all-party committee –'

I saw the light at last. 'Bob, this is terrible.'

'Exactly.'

'Sinister.'

'Precisely.'

'I see the forces of darkness ranged against us. I see tyranny. I see oppression. I see the ancient practice of putting ears to keyholes being outlawed. I see decent, hardworking journalists being jailed for sticking their telephotos through bedroom windows. I see – another drink, Bob?'

'Thanks, Beef, I need one.'

The more I thought about what Bob had said, the more I reckoned he was on to something. A Select Committee on Press Ethics might rank high among the horse-laughs of the decade, but it also spelled trouble. The thing had to be stopped before it got out of hand – and the most effective way of doing this seemed to be to leak the committee's report and rubbish it.

I'm often asked by friends who do proper jobs how journalists get hold of leaked documents. It's a comparatively simple exercise involving a cheque-book, a winning manner and a set of skeleton keys and I've had a good deal of experience. Most leaks fall into one of three categories: the Leak Direct, the Leak Pecuniary and the Leak Unauthorised. The Leak Direct is the most common and also the most satisfying. It's the one a journalist goes for first.

When the committee had finished taking evidence and gone into purdah to draw up its report, I duly got to work. There was a member of the committee called Tony Allsop who was quite a mate of mine and could generally be relied on, if you scratched his back, to do the necessary in return. I tracked him down quaffing a pink gin in Annie's Bar and he greeted me cheerfully.

'What are you drinking, Beef?'

'The usual please, Tony.'

'Got anything good for me?'

I lowered my voice discreetly – there were ladies present. 'Newmarket, three thirty. Fool's Gold. Lovely little two-year-old. Can't miss.'

He grinned and noted the details in his diary. 'Thanks, Beef. I shan't forget it. How's things?'

'Not bad. You?'

'Fine.'

'Jane well?'

'Fine.'

'And the children?'

'Fine.'

'Cheers.'

'Cheers.'

We savoured our drinks in silence. Is there anything to beat the simple dialogue of strong silent men? Then I moved smoothly up a gear.

'How's that committee of yours, Tony?'

'Nearly finished, thank God. We agreed the report yesterday.'

'When's it being published?'

'The week after next.'

'Anything interesting in it?'

Though I say it myself, the question was asked with an air of innocent unconcern which was almost schoolgirlish. I would defy a professional psychologist to have spotted the keen interest behind my nonchalant manner. But these MPs who've been around since the Magna Carta are nobody's fools. Tony chuckled and shook his head.

'Sorry, Beef, you'll have to wait this time. It's all very hush-hush.'

'No chance of a sneak preview for an old friend?'

I gave him one of my appealing looks, but he looked over his shoulder and dropped to a whisper.

'Beef, I'd love to. Honestly. But it's more than my life's worth. The chairman's absolutely insistent the report shouldn't be leaked. He knows there's a lot of media interest, but he's keeping the whole thing under wraps till publication day.'

'What's the problem? You've got your own copy, haven't you? There's a functioning photocopier –'

'Beef, I can't. The chairman's a fanatic. He's had every copy individually numbered and printed on a special colour paper so that, if there's a leak, the culprit can be identified. Mine's turquoise,' he added sourly. 'I can't possibly let you have it.'

I was dumbfounded. I'd never come across such a barbaric practice in my life. It was like a relic of the Dark Ages.

'Understood, Tony,' I said, putting a sympathetic hand on his shoulder. 'These are dangerous times. Men walk the streets in fear. You're just going to have to give me the general gist. What are the main recommendations in the report?'

He gave a careless wave of his hand. 'Oh, I don't remember the *details*. The thing's two hundred paragraphs long. I haven't read most of it. Let's just say your lot are in for a hammering.'

'My lot?'

'The tabloids. The tits-and-bums end of the market. We're proposing some pretty tough measures. Time for you to put your house in order, that sort of thing.'

'You don't remember the specific proposals?'

'What's that? Oh no, not in detail. Sorry, Beef.'

'That's all right, Tony.'

I took my leave in sombre mood. There's no accounting for politicians: you give a man a 10–1 shot at Newmarket and, instead of bending over backwards to help you, he develops galloping amnesia. The horse came in last as things turned out, but that's not the point.

The Leak Direct having failed, I resorted to the Leak Pecuniary. With the sophisticated intelligence network at my disposal, it didn't take long to find out that the report had been typed by one Charlotte Ross, and that Charlotte took lunch in the Strangers cafeteria between one and one thirty.

I found her eating a salad with a fat, battered paperback

15

propped open in front of her. I sat down opposite and she scowled: these girl Fridays may look frightfully self-possessed, but they can only take so many fat, battered objects at one sitting. The scowl hardened as I poured a *roux* of ketchup and mayonnaise on my chips.

'It's Charlotte, isn't it?' I asked, between mouthfuls.

'Yah.'

'Charlotte Ross?'

'Yah.'

The fat paperback had obviously reached a critical point. I had thought my clairvoyance would wow her, coming on top of my suave manner, but she barely looked up from the page. A tough nut to crack.

'I knew your mother,' I said silkily.

'Oh? Yah.'

'Remember me to her, won't you?'

'Yah.'

The paperback continued to hold her attention: from the tiny gasping noises she was making, she seemed to be mid-bedroom scene. I was tempted to say, 'I was close friends with your mother nine months before you were born', which usually sells a few tickets, but native delicacy restrained me. Besides, the story would have lacked conviction. She didn't have the Wellington cheek-bones.

Relief came when she completed the chapter and snapped the book shut.

'I'm sorry, I haven't been listening properly. Did you say you knew Mummy?'

'That's right.'

'I'll tell her. She'll be thrilled. What did you say your name was?'

'George. George Shearer.' I looked mournfully at my stomach. 'She'll remember me as a thin man.'

'I'm so sorry.'

'I've lost my shape, as you can see.'

'You poor thing.'

'Don't mention it. If I was quite frank with you, Charlotte' – I added more mayonnaise to my chips and took a gulp of beer – 'I have to take some of the blame myself.'

It was a gamble, playing this particular card, but my history interested her strangely. These girls look tough as nails, but wring their withers in the right place and they're there for the taking. Her gaze softened and she studied me with something close to pity.

'Have you ever tried going on a diet, Mr Shearer?'

'George.'

'George.'

'Oh, frequently, frequently.' I took another gulp of beer and addressed my dessert. 'Scarsdale, Cambridge, Oxford, A-plan, G-plan, high-fibre, low-fibre, you name it. I practically starve myself, then, just as I think I'm winning, I suddenly lose heart. Isn't life cruel?'

Yah, she agreed, it was cruel.

'All that human possibility wasted because I can't find the strength to say no.'

'How awful.'

'It's just one of those things.' She was well and truly on my side by now, so I changed tack expertly. 'Where are you working now, by the way?'

'For something called the Committee on Press Ethics. Why?'

'How fascinating. I used to have a friend who was a journalist. He did very well, then the excitement became too much and he turned to accountancy. Isn't that lot about to produce a big report?'

'Don't,' she said, pulling a face. 'I've just finished typing the bloody thing.'

'You haven't.'

'I have. There's pages and pages of it and it's so *boring*. I thought I'd die doing it.'

'You poor thing.'

'Don't mention it.'

We looked each other in the eyes: one of those moments of perfect human sympathy. My weight problem, her boring job: we had suffered in different ways and suffered in the same way; the world had been cruel to both of us. I had engineered things perfectly.

'Tell me,' I said, maintaining eye-contact and reaching across to take her hand. 'If I were to offer you £300 –'

English syntax is a tricky thing and on a paper like mine you don't get much practice. Ten-word sentences are the order of the day and, if you try anything fancy, the sub-editors pounce on it like tigers. The sentence forming on my lips was, 'If I were to offer you £300, could you let me have a copy of the report?' Perfectly grammatical and a princely offer for the document in question. But I should have rephrased it. 'Would you let me have a copy of the report if I offered you £300?' might or mightn't have brought home the bacon. I shall never know. But it would certainly have averted a major misunderstanding.

Upon the mention of money, her mouth dropped open and her eyes blazed in indignation. Before you could say Benjamin Disraeli, she had stormed out of the room. And it didn't stop there. The line 'You could offer me a million and I wouldn't go to bed with you, you fat creep,' is good box-office at the best of times: delivered at eight decibels in a crowded cafeteria, with a rising inflection on 'million', 'bed' and 'creep', the effect is sensational. There was a silence you could cut with a knife and two lantern-jawed policemen converged on me . . .

I mustn't boast, but it says a lot for the resourcefulness of the tabloid press that, within half an hour of this little set-back, I was in Tim Glazebury's room committing an act of larceny. The Leak Unauthorised it was going to have to be.

The room was in a remote corridor underneath the kitchens where they house ex-Prime Ministers, chairmen of procedure committees and junior Opposition Whips who have fallen on hard times. A dingy little rabbit-hutch, not more than ten foot square, with mountains of old papers on the floor and a lingering smell of coffee. It took me about ten minutes to dig out the report and, as I was anxious to hear the worst, I settled down to read it on the spot. Prime

Minister's Questions were just starting in the House, there was a big statement on Hong Kong to follow, so I reckoned I was good for at least an hour.

I don't know if you've ever visited the Chamber of Horrors at Madame Tussaud's, but reading that report did very similar things to the digestive system. It was like looking into the darkest corner of the human soul and seeing the extraordinary atrocities of which man was capable when he rolled up his sleeves and applied himself. The thing was a compound of ingenuity and malevolence: there was one particularly sinister paragraph (on the subject of leaks, curiously) where I had to loosen my collar to arrest a rising wave of nausea.

It was written in a lofty mandarin style and I won't trouble you with the contents. Suffice to say that, if only half the recommendations had reached the statute book, it would have spelled the end of the tabloid press as we know and love it. The art of gracefully eliding fiction and non-fiction which has made our newspapers the envy of the world stood in danger of extinction. Heavy fines were proposed for just about everything. Newspaper editors were to be electronically tagged. And, if I read paragraph eighty-one correctly, any poor hack who alleged a sexual relationship between A and B without signed affidavits from both parties and a full video recording was in danger of ending his days sewing mail-bags in Wormwood Scrubs.

Particularly offensive was the reference to myself. 'Our conviction that the activities of the popular press need to be more strictly regulated was reinforced by the evidence given by Mr Wellington. This witness appeared to believe that, so long as he entertained, he could write what he liked. We found this line of argument pretty thin.' Thin? *Thin*? I could see that one doing the rounds for weeks and I didn't like it.

At this moment voices were raised at the other end of the corridor. As a journalist's life is only bearable if he avoids getting caught *in flagrante delicto*, I shoved back the report where I had found it and made good my escape.

*

There was a message back at my desk to ring Brian Sparkes, our esteemed editor: a bird-brained little greaser who insists on his subordinates calling him 'Chief'. The message said URGENT, so I went off to the bar for a quick one and made contact three hours later. He seemed pissed off for some reason.

'Where the hell have you been, Beef?'

'Working.'

'Is that what you call it?'

'Making enquiries. Asking questions. Taking soundings. Monitoring developments. Keeping my ear close to the ground. The usual stuff.'

'You've been drinking, haven't you?'

'I have. The House of Commons isn't a monastery. If you want to keep your ear close to the ground, you have to have a drink in your hand.'

'Well, you'd better sober up fast. I want you to do the Hampstead run tonight.'

'Did you say the Hampstead run?'

'Yes.'

'You want *me* to do the Hampstead run?'

'Yes.'

I drew myself up to my full height and gave a masterful scowl. So much wasted effort, of course, with Brian ten miles away, but it seemed to help.

'I won't do it, Chief.'

'You fucking will.'

'I fucking won't. I'm the parliamentary correspondent, not our man in Upper Volta. It's quite outrageous to ask a man of my age and physique to do the Hampstead run. Why can't one of the boys on the foreign news desk do it?'

'Three of them are on leave.'

'Or the sports desk?'

'It's the semi-final replay. Beef, I wouldn't normally ask, but we're short-staffed tonight. There's nothing happening in the House.'

'What do you mean, nothing? There's the second reading

of the Miscellaneous Financial Provisions (Scotland) Bill.'

'Bugger that.'

'Followed by a motion on the Animal Feedingstuffs (Amendment) (No 2) Regulations.' I sighed. 'I would have to concede that the House of Commons has seen glitzier nights.'

'There you are then. Hampstead it is. I'll give you a bonus, of course.'

'How much?'

'Three hundred.'

'Could you make it six?'

'All right, you bastard. But you'll do it?'

'With gritted teeth. By the way,' I said, suddenly remembering, 'I've seen the Report on Press Ethics.'

He chuckled. 'Good man, Beef. That's what we pay you for. What's it like? A turkey?'

'A turkey with teeth. One of the most alarming documents I've ever read. If it goes through, newspapers will be back where they were in Russia in Jo Stalin's heyday. Shall I phone in the details tomorrow?'

'Yes, please.'

'But for the moment it's Hampstead Ho?'

'Thank you, Beef.'

'Don't mention it.'

I suspect that, if I don't fill in more of the background to this story, you're going to jump ship and do the ironing instead. So here goes.

The Hampstead run was one of those tedious chores with which a journalist's life abounds. It didn't involve running or I wouldn't have been asked, but it did involve Hampstead – half fact and half fiction, in other words, like the rest of the tabloid *oeuvre*. Rumours had been circulating of unspecified depravities taking place in the dead of night on Hampstead Heath and our editor wanted us to be the first to tell the world what sort of depravities they were. Every night now for three months a reporter had been solemnly dispatched to the scene on the off-chance of landing a scoop.

To date the only suspicious findings were a used condom, some unidentified squirrel droppings and cyclists riding without lights. But the editor was a stubborn bugger and wasn't letting up. And so the long summer wore on.

I didn't propose to exert myself on the assignment. I took a taxi to Jack Straw's Castle, settled down at a corner table and oiled my larynx till closing time with assorted wines and spirits. Then I staggered out of the pub and crossed the road towards the heath. It was a moonless night with rain in the air, so there was no point in overdoing things. I heaved myself a few hundred yards into the interior, sank down on a bench and smoked a cigarette. Then I must have fallen asleep. When I woke, it was three in the morning, the moon was shining brightly and the air was filled with voices.

I sat up with a start. The voices were coming from over my left shoulder, to the north of the heath. I went to investigate. This involved fighting through the undergrowth, tripping over a log, banging my head against a lamppost and scrambling through a small stagnant pond.

There's a lot of nonsense talked about journalists and, of all the cock-eyed myths surrounding the profession, none is more absurd than the notion that we lead a glamorous life. I meet this everywhere. I'm at a cocktail party talking to a woman. She's looking over my shoulder for someone with a bit more fizz. I announce that I'm a journalist. She says, did you say journalist? I say, yes, journalist. She says, you mean, *journalist*? I say, yes, that very animal. And immediately she stops staring into the middle distance and hangs on my every word as if I've just got back from the Lebanon with shrapnel in my leg. Extraordinary.

Nobody watching me that night could have nursed any such illusions. As I reached the scene of the action and crawled into a bush to escape observation, arriving at the same time as a colony of man-eating ants, the £600 bonus I'd demanded seemed laughably inadequate.

In front of me, in a clearing in the wood, a crowd of about forty had gathered. Middle-aged men mainly, with their coats buttoned up to their collars and a furtive look on their faces. Civil servants, no doubt, publishers, surveyors, the odd clergyman. They looked like punters at a private screening of *Hot Convent Nights*, although their real purpose was more sinister – as was evidenced by the burly man with a moustache on the qui vive, mastiff-like, at the entrance to the clearing.

They were grouped in a circle, so it took me a while to work out what was happening in the middle. When I did, I nearly had a heart seizure. There was a sudden muffled roar, shouts of 'Get at it!' and 'Come on, my beauty!' and, before you knew it, two bantam cocks were tearing each other to pieces. It was worse than a Cabinet meeting.

I'm not an animal-lover myself, being of the view that the place for our furry friends is on a plate surrounded by potatoes and *béarnaise* sauce, but I've been at the business long enough to know a good story when I see one. I whipped out a pocket camera (regulation issue on my paper) and got to work. The ants were proceeding up my trouser legs with the air of ants who hadn't had their dinner, but I hardly noticed them.

Now that the perpetrators of this outrage are being detained at Her Majesty's pleasure, I can fairly claim to be a national hero. But what really bucked me, what really persuaded me that life on the Street of Shame had its compensating sweetnesses, was the identity of the diminutive man in a cloth cap who, from the way he kept waving his arms like a traffic warden, was the master of ceremonies.

Timothy Hall Glazebury, MP.

The day the Report on Press Ethics was published, the heavens opened and it rained furiously from first light. Victoria Street was a sea of umbrellas and people slid like ice-skaters across the pavements in Parliament Square. It might have been an omen.

A press conference had been called for twelve o'clock in the Grand Committee Room off Westminster Hall. Journalists who turned up early were allowed to read 'confidential revise' copies in advance – this is the usual form – and there was quite a scrum for the facility. I had already leaked the sexier bits of the report, but this only seemed to heighten the general excitement. My confrères just couldn't believe the report was as awful as I claimed; when they got their paws on their own copies and saw that it was, there was a collective intake of breath followed by a low growling noise. I haven't seen such a sorry-looking press corps since the drinks ran out at Monty Egerton's memorial service.

At twelve on the dot, Alan Price, the chairman, marched on to the rostrum followed by various other members of the committee: Sally Charlton, the token woman; Mike Grimes, the token intellectual; Sir Jeremy Bicester, the token nob – and Glazebury. He was barely recognisable as the man in a cloth cap supervising the cock-fight on Hampstead Heath, but you know how it is: take a man out of his natural environment and he's a lost thing.

'Good morning, ladies and gentlemen,' Alan Price announced, in his usual crisp style. 'You've got your copies of our report now, so I don't have to say much by way of preamble. We don't expect our recommendations to win us many friends in Fleet Street, but we're not answerable to Fleet Street, we're answerable to our constituents. And there's a general feeling in the country that the traditional freedoms of the press have been so widely abused that something has to be done about it. We've made a few, we hope constructive, suggestions as to what that something should be. It's a tough report, but we believe it's a fair report and a balanced report. And we're confident that the Government will give very serious consideration to implementing it. Are there any questions? Yes, Mr Hancock?'

Tiger asked the question which was bothering all of us.

'Are you really saying in paragraph eighty-seven that journalists who don't check their facts properly might be fined?'

'That's exactly what we're saying. Only in extreme circumstances, obviously.'

'Don't you think that's pretty draconian?'

'We think it's fair. All we're trying to do is ensure greater accountability. Yes, Mr Macdonald?'

'How do you rate the chances of the Government accepting your recommendations?'

'We think the great majority of them will prove acceptable. The Home Secretary will be responding in due course. Yes, Mr Jones?'

'Most of your criticisms seem to be directed at the tabloids. Are you holding them responsible for the main abuses you've identified?'

'That's correct. We were very unimpressed by what they said in justification of their attitudes. I might add –'

This was too much for a man of my sensitivity. I heaved myself to my feet and let them have it. 'Can I put a question to Mr Glazebury please, Chairman?'

'Go ahead.'

'Would I be exaggerating if I said he was as mad as a fighting cock at the way the media have been treating him?'

It was a happy choice of simile. Nobody else batted an eyelid, but Glazebury went the colour of a tomato and looked at me with alarm.

'No,' he muttered. 'I don't accept that.'

'If, for example, he were to be engaged in bizarre and illegal practices involving animals and a journalist reported the fact, would he say that was irresponsible journalism?'

'That rather depends –'

'I'm thinking specifically of recent events on Hampstead Heath. These pictures will illustrate my point.'

I took the photographs out of my pocket and started passing them round. The meeting broke up in grave disorder ten minutes later.

The next morning's edition of my paper was a fine example of the news coverage which has won us prizes all over Europe. COCK HORROR PROBE, ran the main headline; a short paragraph on page thirteen notified readers that a report on press ethics had been published. What was particularly gratifying was the way other papers followed our lead. In the general outcry about Glazebury, the details of the report went largely unreported and, when the House came to debate it three months later, there was an audience of eleven and the show folded early. I believe the report's now gathering dust in a basement in the Home Office.

Glazebury was chucked out of the House, served a short term in jug and went to earth in darkest Warwickshire. Two years later, quite by chance, I ran into him at a dinner in Nuneaton. It could have been an awkward reunion, but time seemed to have healed the old wounds. Over the main course – *coq au vin*, funnily – he explained that he'd only got involved with the Hampstead racket because he was so bored with his life. I said I was bored with my life and suggested various alternative stimulants which he promised to consider. We had quite a chat.

The fact is, I've got nothing against politicians so long as they sell newspapers.

2

COLONEL'S FOXY LADY!

The fact that Colonel Sir Walter Hockley-Giles MP, a ruddy-faced, moustachioed man who spent his Saturdays potting pheasants and chasing foxes across the West Riding of Yorkshire, was having a torrid affair with red-haired Brummie Lynn Todd, Member of Parliament for a very different party and well-known animal rights activist, struck my simple journalist's mind as a snippet of information which deserved a wider audience. The public had a right to know – as we hacks say when we're caught with our ear to the keyhole of life's little naughtinesses.

I put the point to Brian Sparkes, my editor, who saw the possibilities in the story right away. BIZARRE SECRET OF FOXY LADY. You could see him doing captions in his head. He's got the best nose for the stuff in the business. But he was in cautious mood. We'd just been stung for fifty grand by an actress contesting our claim that she'd had a face-lift – she hadn't, but the story read well and it was August – so the paper was going through one of its virtuous phases when facts had to be checked. They don't last long.

'Define torrid affair,' he said, doodling on the back of an envelope with a green felt-tip which he periodically put in his mouth to masticate.

'You mean . . . ?'

'What exactly are we talking about here? Let's go back to first principles.'

I stared at him. We were clapped-out hacks from the grubbier end of the Street of Shame: we didn't have any principles, first or second. I explained in Anglo-Saxon monosyllables with matching hand-gestures what I meant by an affair. He nodded dourly. 'Torrid', I went on, was by way of embellishment since I hadn't actually seen the happy couple at it. In my experience 'tepid' was more often the *mot juste* for the sexual act; but since the only ones who knew that were the two parties concerned and they were usually happy to have their prowess exaggerated in print, it was conventional in the popular press . . .

'I don't want semantics, Beef, I want facts. Are these two jokers having it off or aren't they?'

'Of course they are. I've seen them at it.'

'Where?'

'In the National Gallery.'

'That place on Trafalgar Square? What, kissing? Holding hands?'

'Of course not. They're not stupid. They were looking at a painting of the Crucifixion. By some dead Iti.'

'So how . . . ?'

I fixed him with a stern look. 'Chief, this is madness. Use your common sense. Would *you* go the National Gallery with a woman if you weren't bonking her?'

'You know I wouldn't,' he conceded. 'Of course not, of course not. This Hockley-Giles character,' he went on, swivelling his chair round and staring into the middle distance past the dome of St Paul's. 'How old is he?'

'Sixty-eight. Been in the House since the Flood. A real political dinosaur. There was a Euthanasia Bill last year and someone suggested he should declare an interest. He's retiring at the next election.'

'What are his politics?'

'Party loyalist. As honest as the day is long and as thick as the plank is wide.'

'Family?'

'Six children. Very rich or very Catholic. Maybe both. I could check.'

'And the girl?'

'Thirty, thirty-five. First Parliament. Chain-smoker, veg-etarian, single. Ambitious as hell. Goes in for leather jackets and single earrings.'

'Kinky.'

'The whole thing's kinky. It will keep politics off the front page for weeks. What about it, Chief?'

He swivelled his chair back to face me. 'Get me every-thing you can on it, Beef. The whole dirt. Oh and, Beef,' he called after me as I turned to leave. 'What the hell were you doing in the National Gallery yourself?'

'I thought it was a wine-bar,' I said – quite truthfully – and ambled off in search of lunch.

There's a school of thought, to which I don't subscribe, which favours a light lunch. Go easy till the evening and then enjoy yourself. But how can you enjoy yourself if you're out of training? I've never understood that. Surely the thing about a large lunch is that it sets you up nicely for an even larger dinner. Opens the arteries and so on. I take the same view of breakfast.

So I ordered a second helping of *tortellini* and, staying ahead of the game, cast an eye over the sweet trolley. It was one fifteen and I had an hour to kill. Mario replenished my wineglass with a smile. '*Buon appetito*, Signor Beef.' Nice lad, Mario. Born in Hackney, never been further than Boulogne, but the best Italian accent in SW1. Doesn't hold it against a customer if he weighs over the odds and looks like a mistake in the chemistry lab. Just keeps bringing the pasta and smiling. There should be more like him.

'Ever take a woman to an art gallery, Mario?' I asked when he brought the *tortellini*. He looked puzzled, then sheepish.

'*Si*, signor. Once, in Oxford . . .'

'Were you lovers?'

'*Si*, signor. Why . . . ?'

'Thank you, Mario.'

I sipped thoughtfully at my wine. I was right, I had to

29

be right. If a journalist can't trust his nose, he shouldn't be a journalist. But how was I going to rustle up the salacious details which my sex-crazed readership demanded? I was a lobby correspondent, not a gofer on the gossip page. These clandestine affairs were a closed book to me: I'd given up sex when I passed sixteen stone and, as a spectator sport, it had palled. I was out of my depth.

I stopped Mario again as he poured the cream on my dessert.

'That girl in Oxford, Mario. Did you, uh, make love before or after you went to the gallery? What I'm getting at is, how does art fit into the whole sex caboodle?'

'Both, signor. Before and after. We were young.'

'And if you hadn't been young?'

'I think probably after only.'

'Thank you, Mario. That's very helpful. Some people do see life, don't they?'

He brought me my two bills – one for £20 to settle, another for £40 to claim on expenses (you've got to peculate to accumulate, as my granny used to say) – and I padded off to a bookmaker with the proceeds. A nice lad, Mario. Who said the black economy wasn't what it used to be?

It was Welsh Office Questions in the House, so the Press Gallery was a desert and there was no sign of Hockley-Giles or Lynn Todd on the benches. I retired to the bar to watch the two forty-five from Towcester with the better element, then drifted back into the Chamber for Prime Minister's Questions.

I was having trouble focusing, but a row of some description about the economy seemed to be hotting up nicely. The Leader of the Opposition called the Prime Minister a by-word for incompetence (that's Commons-speak for someone who can't organise a piss-up in a brewery) and the heavy mob below the gangway bayed for his resignation. All good clean family entertainment. Various Government backbenchers leapt to their feet.

'Sir Walter Hockley-*Giles*!' the Speaker called out, to

general derision. Unfair really, if you go in for fairness and I don't much. I mean, it's not his fault he's got a silly name, is it?

'Does my Right Honourable friend *agree . . .*' rose a booming voice from the far end of the Chamber, at which the derision became so operatic it drowned what he was saying. (Pterodactyls like H-G never ask real questions: they just thunder one of their pet prejudices and pop a question mark on the end.) The Prime Minister said his Honourable friend had made a valid point. Prolonged jeering. A bearded Opposition Member asked a question about river pollution. Hoots of laughter, this time from the Government side. These parliamentary jokes are terribly funny once you've got the hang of them. The trouble is, once you've got the hang of them, you don't find them funny any more. It's sad.

I glanced across to the other side of the Chamber. Lynn was sitting in the third row back, just above the gangway, drinking it all in, listening to every word – the sure sign of a new Member. I noticed she joined in the jeering at H-G's 'question', but that meant nothing. She would, wouldn't she?

After Questions, she introduced a ten-minute rule Bill – called ten-minute rule Bills because the Member introducing them has just ten minutes to put his/her case. One of the best Standing Orders of a bad lot, I've always thought. If you can't do something in ten minutes, it's not worth doing. I exclude having lunch.

Lynn's Bill was called the Blood Sports (Prohibition) Bill and she banged on about our furry friends and how inhuman it was to chase them across the countryside on horseback, then let packs of dogs tear them to pieces. X-certificate stuff, and I was about to retire to the bar for a sedative when I noticed something.

Most of the other Members had made for the EXIT sign as soon as she rose to speak. It's always the way after Prime Minister's Questions: the next speaker has to battle against the odds, like a comedian coming on after the stripper. But

31

there was one man listening very intently indeed: Sir Walter Hockley-Giles.

If I describe this old reprobate as an open book, you'll know what I'm getting at. He's one of those simple souls with no taste for dissimulation: you can tell exactly what he's feeling at a given moment. And his feelings now were all too obvious. As Lynn chuntered on about foxes' finer feelings, a kind of reverence glowed in his cheeks; he hung upon her every word; he wheezed and spluttered at her every joke. You expected the Speaker to tell him to pull himself together or leave the Chamber: it was that bad. And this, remember, from the most unrepentant chivier of foxes since Siegfried Sassoon. Ghastly.

It was all the confirmation I needed. A man and a woman can go to the National Gallery together and, at a pinch and with good will on both sides, remain celibate. But that anyone could listen to Lynn speaking with a lovesick gaze on his face if there wasn't a deal of nooky in the offing, defied belief. Her rhetorical skills began and ended with the ability to mouth a simple English sentence in the right order without falling over her feet. It wasn't her oratory which had kindled the colonel's fires, it was her. There could be no possible doubt.

I went looking for H-G when he left the Chamber. There's a corridor leading from the Members Lobby to the Tea Room much favoured by lobby correspondents on the prowl and, in my case, indispensable. It's only six feet wide and, when I station myself in the middle, that leaves eighteen inches either side. The buggers have to talk to me.

H-G greeted me without enthusiasm. He's never quite forgiven me for telling the story of the barmaid's dog, of which more another time, and takes a pretty dim view of hacks generally. There are several Members like that, I don't know why.

'Afternoon, Beef,' he growled, trying to squeeze past me on the left or Tea Room side.

'Afternoon, Walter,' I parried, wedging him against the wall. 'Can I have a word?'

'Go ahead, young man.' I'm fifty-three, by the way, but this sort of gag goes down a treat in his part of Yorkshire.

'This Blood Sports Bill of Lynn Todd's.'

He shot me a suspicious look. 'What about it?'

'Are you going to vote against it on second reading?'

'Course I am.'

'You think it's a non-starter?'

'Course it is. Fox-hunting's been a part of rural life for hundreds of years. The trouble with these anti-hunting loonies is they don't know the first thing about the countryside.'

'So you think Lynn Todd's an anti-hunting loony?'

I took a notebook out of my pocket, at which his jaw sagged and he looked at me with a wild surmise.

'Ah well, no, you mustn't quote me on that, Beef. That was off the record. I've nothing against the lady personally, you understand. Perfectly pleasant. Perfectly, ah, personable and all that.'

'So you *don't* think she's a loony?'

'Not for a minute, no. Spoke out of turn.'

'It's her *views* that are loony?'

'Ye-es.'

'A nice, normal girl with mentally unhinged opinions?'

'Sort of. Look, Beef . . .' He dithered and I stood with pencil poised, looking dumb. It's the oldest trick in the game, but the punters buy it every time.

'Excuse me please,' came a woman's voice behind me. (A problem with this corridor, as you'll know if you've done your arithmetic, is that if I'm talking to anyone more than six inches wide, nobody else can get past.) I turned to make room. It was Lynn. Earring, leather jacket, the works.

'Afternoon, Lynn.'

'Afternoon, Beef.'

'Afternoon, Lynn.'

'Afternoon, Walter.'

'How are you keeping, Lynn?'

'Fine, Walter. You?'

'Fine, thanks.'

Pretty chummy stuff, you'll agree. There's a school of thought in the great blue yonder that politicians are cold fish and never make friends with other politicians because it would make it awkward to stab them in the back if they had broken bread with them beforehand. Not a bit of it. There's a bonhomie in the House of Commons at its best which recalls the merry cut and thrust in the back row of the coach on a Rotary Club outing. It does a man's heart good to see.

But something in this latest exchange jarred. A bit stilted, a bit wooden, if you know what I mean. The two of them acted as if my presence was an encumbrance – which I suppose, if my theory was right and they would have preferred to be holding the conversation minus clothes and minus one large lobby correspondent, it was. I tried to jolly things along by telling an off-colour joke I'd heard from the man on the *Gloucestershire Times*, but they wouldn't play ball, just shuffled their feet. So I took direct action.

'What's up, Lynn?' I asked smoothly. 'You look as if you're hiding something. Dirty work at the crossroads?'

'Shove it, Beef.'

'Backbench revolt?'

'Shove it.'

I love Brummies: they are so straightforward. She was half smiling but, more to the point, half blushing. Promising. As my old mentor Charlie Dudgeon used to say: when you've got a politician to blush, you can start sharpening your pencil.

There were no corresponding signs on H-G's face but, as the party broke up, I heard him say to Lynn, in a matter-of-fact voice: 'Is it a two-liner tonight or three?'

'Three till ten, then two.'

Which set me thinking.

But first some interpretation for my English readers. At the start of each week's parliamentary business, Members are sent a piece of paper by their party Whips indicating when they will be required to vote. If an item of business is underlined three times, it means that, if the Member

34

wishes his head to remain joined to his body and not lopped off and thrown into the Thames, his presence is essential – a 'three-line whip'. Two-line whips and one-line whips are correspondingly less urgent and Members can 'pair' with their opposite numbers, i.e. make a prior arrangement with a Member of the other main party that neither of them will vote. Hence the significance of the exchange between H-G and *la* Todd: they would have to stay in the House till the ten o'clock vote, but could then push off together with the Whips' blessing. All very interesting in the circumstances.

There was obviously nothing to be done for a few hours, so I went down to Annie's and dug myself in for the duration. Lennie was there, Tom, Bill, Arthur, the usual crowd. It's a hard slog being a lobby correspondent on a paper which ranks politics between bingo and 'You and Your Stars'. There's a lot of sitting round waiting for things to happen and, if you don't have a hobby to keep you going, like staring into a glass of whisky and talking about the good old days, your head can start to drop. At half past six the Health Minister dropped in and, with the help of a few doubles, started being indiscreet: this necessitated a trip to the Press Gallery to phone copy through to my paper. 'Highly placed sources in the Department of Health have confirmed . . .' You don't mention that the sources have had a skinful because it would look bad: you leave that to the readers' common sense. It's all in a day's work.

At quarter to ten, I made my way up to the Gallery. The Chamber was packed to the gills and the Chancellor was making the closing speech for the Government. Don't ask me what the debate was about. When you've been in the House as long as I have, you know it's not what MPs are saying that makes news, but what they aren't saying. Politicians with their trousers on don't sell newspapers. Sad, but true.

My two beauties were in their usual places. Lynn joined in the Opposition shouts of 'Disgraceful!' as the Chancellor explained his latest forecasting cock-up. H-G lent his weight to the Government roars of 'Withdraw!' Two red-blooded

35

political animals, as fine as you could hope to see. At ten, the division was called and they filed into their respective lobbies to vote. I went down to the car park, drove up to New Palace Yard and parked in the shadows under Big Ben. The trap was set.

At five minutes past, H-G appeared and joined the queue of Members waiting for taxis. At seven minutes past, Lynn followed. They nodded to each other, but didn't say anything. A taxi drove into the yard, then another. H-G was now at the front of the queue. As his cab approached, he turned and called out: 'Can I take anyone to Bayswater?' Lynn stepped smoothly forward. 'I'm Paddington.' A stickler would have asked to see her duffelcoat, but that's by the by. H-G opened the door of the cab for her and they got in together. As easy as drinking Scotch before breakfast. None of the other Members in the queue batted an eyelid. Why should they?

I set off in pursuit in my P reg Ford Escort. This antique will never pass fifty again, but it's done me proud: it's custom-built to take the excess baggage in the driver's seat and allow me to enter and leave the car without tangling with the steering-wheel. The taxi drove along Birdcage Walk, up Constitution Hill and round Hyde Park Corner. In Park Lane it slowed to a crawl in the after-theatre traffic and I could see Lynn and H-G cooing and billing in the back seat. First she cooed and he billed, then the other way round, then they both cooed together. By Marble Arch they were practically singing *Cavalleria Rusticana*. It was lovely just watching them.

The taxi turned off the Bayswater Road and pulled up outside a large terraced house. H-G got out first, paid the cabbie, glanced over his shoulder and opened the front door; there was a fractional pause, then Lynn shot in after him like an animal going to cover. I felt really chuffed. People say journalists are lazy, but I'd driven two and a half miles during opening hours to get this story and I'd read the situation perfectly. Now for the hard bit.

I don't know if you've ever tried observing Members of

Parliament in their bedrooms? No? Well, take a tip from an old campaigner and only take the job if you're being paid doubloons by the sackful. It's not worth it otherwise. Politicians are retiring creatures and like to spend their eight hours horizontal, either alone or with a companion of their choice: if they see a representative of the Fourth Estate staring at them through the curtains while they are in bed with no clothes on, they can get quite shirty. I learnt this as a cub reporter when I was chased round a garden in Hampstead by Sir James Halifax's Alsatian. He simply wouldn't acknowledge the philosophical point that I was just doing my job – Sir James, I mean, not the dog, who was probably quite a rational animal if you got past the snapping and barking stage, which I didn't. It's a bit rich, isn't it? How these people's tribunes – who spend every waking hour trying to bend the ear of the media and come toadying up in the House of Commons with the most flatulent comments and expect to see them printed, never mind the pin-up girls and the horoscopes and the real news – how they have the nerve to cry foul if you check up on their sex lives, is quite beyond me.

I was mulling over these great questions of principle when, through a gap in the bedroom curtains, I caught my first sight of Sir Walter Hockley-Giles's boxer shorts. I nearly dropped dead in shock. To say they were white with a pattern of pink winged pigs and OINK, OINK! emblazoned in scarlet across the upper groin would convey the letter, not the spirit, of their awfulness. They were a nightmare. They would have seared the retina from twenty yards at an exhibition of modern painting. I'd seen similar eyesores in shop windows, but assumed they were intended as Christmas presents for weak-minded teenagers. To see them girding the loins of a former Master of Hounds of the oldest hunt in Yorkshire was a spectacle to unman the stoutest.

They completely upstaged the other tourist attraction in the room, which was Lynn Todd naked in bed smoking a six-inch cigar with one hand and stroking a ginger cat with the other. I had secured a front-row seat by taking advantage of an adjacent fire-escape and crawling on hands and knees across a flat roof. It was risky, but you don't see life by sitting at home and, if I wasn't seeing life now, I don't know what I was seeing. The window was open a crack, which meant I had a sound-track, but the script was so frightful I think I'd have preferred the silent version.

'Who's a silly boy then?' Lynn asked in a gooey voice. 'Who's the silliest, naughtiest boy in London?'

I thought she was addressing H-G, who was still struggling out of his boxer shorts, but it seemed the cat was the object of her attentions, for he gave a little purr and snuggled under her armpit. I scouted round for somewhere to be sick.

'Beautiful creature, isn't he?' said H-G, his boxer shorts trapped round his upper thighs. They were between six and seven sizes too small for him.

'He's lovely.'

'I've had him nearly ten years.'

'He's got such beautiful little eyes.'

'He's like a child to me really.'

'And those adorable whiskers.'

'I don't know what I'd do without him.'

The boxer shorts hadn't budged. He swore under his breath and hopped across the room to a chair. Lynn took the cat in her arms and kissed it on the nose. 'Who's a lovely little pussy-wussy then?' Even the cat was beginning to wear an embarrassed air.

By now practical as well as aesthetic considerations were bothering me. I had put a small tape-recorder near the window, meaning to bequeath the conversation to posterity, but it was only a half-hour tape and was rapidly filling up with the sort of bilge my editor threw straight in the bin. Members of Parliament talking popcorn about animals don't land in the soup, they double their majorities. And that wasn't the objective.

At this point, mercifully, Lynn spotted that all wasn't well with her loved one's lingerie.

'Are you having trouble with those, Walt?'

'Just a touch. I don't seem –'

'Here, let me.'

They pulled together, there was a loud rending sound and one eyesore was replaced by another: the Member for North-West Yorkshire standing in all his glory before the Member for South-East Birmingham in all her glory. Not pretty, not what the voters had voted for. It put me in mind of an illustration I'd once seen in an abridged version of *The Origin of Species*.

'Oh Walt.'

'Oh Lynn.'

'Oh Walt.'

'Oh Lynn.'

I relaxed and settled back to watch. It wasn't Shakespeare, but it would make a damn good read over the cornflakes. Twenty more minutes of this and, if the cat stayed out of things, it would be one of my very best efforts. Woodward and Bernstein, eat your heart out.

But the cat didn't stay out of things. Moved by what psychiatrists call the 'excluded third' syndrome, he launched himself across the room and interposed his attentions between the elected Members. H-G said something unparliamentary, but Lynn again scooped the creature up in her arms and pussie-wussied it. Then she waxed philosophical. You could see her point. The sight of H-G in the buff was one to make the raunchiest female re-examine her priorities and, if a few minutes' respite could be bought by wittering about cats, most women in Lynn's position would have gone for the feline option. Frustrating for the watching press corps, but there you have it. From the moony look on her face, I had a sinking feeling she was about to ask H-G if cats had souls.

'Walt, do you think cats have souls?' There, I told you. You can always trust a journalist.

'What's that? Souls, you say?'

H-G, I have to report, entered the conversation without much vim. Having fought his way out of the boxer shorts, the old soldier's energies were directed to a single end.

'Yes, you know. Do you think there's a part of them that lives on after they're dead or is that it?'

'Is that what?'

'Is death death?'

'What?'

'Death. Is it or isn't it?'

'Is death . . . ?'

He was struggling, no question. Intellectually, you would normally place H-G between an estate agent and a cauliflower: bamboozled with fancy-talk just as he was about to get his rocks off, the vegetable side of the brain predominated. But he was the decent, chivalrous, old-fashioned sort. He could no more have told Lynn to go and see a doctor about her problems than flown to the moon. If she wanted to talk fruitcake, she must talk fruitcake. And she did. Oodles and oodles of the stuff.

'What I'm getting at is this, Walt. You're a nice, kind man who loves his cat and looks after it and says it's like a child and so on. But you're quite happy to spend your weekends killing foxes and pheasants and all sorts of other animals. How do you square that? What's your intellectual position? What do you really believe? Do you think animals are intrinsically inferior to us, so we can do what we want with them? Or do you see them as real, living, breathing, feeling, loving –'

'Oh, get a fucking move on.' This was my own contribution, I hasten to add: H-G wasn't in the NUJ and didn't talk to women like that. I meant to mutter it under my breath, but Lynn stopped mid-sentence and stared at the curtains.

'Did you hear something, Walt?'

'I don't think so, darling.'

'I could have sworn . . .'

'It must have been the wind.'

'I'll take a look.'

We journalists are brave as lions in normal circumstances, but we know the value of a strategic retreat. In younger days I would have retrieved the tape-recorder, legged it to the nearest pub and settled down to write the story over a large whisky. In the event, my sudden backward movement placed an intolerable strain on the flat roof where I was crouching. It had been constructed, I would guess, in the late 1890s and the builders had set themselves no more ambitious task than to keep the rain out of the room below and provide a resting-place for pigeons, blackbirds and the odd cat. To take the full weight of a roving reporter wasn't part of its brief – and I duly plummeted ten feet or so on to the matrimonial bed of Mr and Mrs Simon Arbuthnott, barristers-at-law.

Their names and professions didn't immediately advertise themselves. In the general confusion I was conscious only of a woman screaming in the dark and a man saying 'What the hell . . . ?' in a strangulated, hooray-Henry sort of voice.

I stepped gingerly off the bed and dusted myself down. 'I'm terribly sorry. I seem to have fallen through your roof.' Good, that one, I thought. Polite, factual, to the point. It's what journalists are paid for.

A bedside light came on and, from underneath a quantity of rubble, plaster and pigeon-droppings, a young, rather attractive couple stared up at me. She slim, brunette, Laura Ashley nightdress. He tall, light-heavyweight, pyjamas in rather violent navy. Drop in on any bedroom in that part of town and you'll see much the same.

'What were you doing on the roof to start with?' asked the male half of the duet. A very fair question. I could tell I was dealing with a legal mind.

'I was chasing a burglar.'

'Did you catch him?'

'It was a pigeon.'

'But you *thought* you saw a burglar?'

'It must have been a trick of the light.'

'Now, look here, Mr –'

'Althorp. Toby Althorp.'

He took his Filofax out of the drawer beside the bed and

asked me to spell the name. His wife stared mesmerised at my stomach.

'You're rather . . . big to be chasing about on roofs, aren't you?'

'Big? I'm only five foot nine.'

'What I mean is, Mr –'

'Arlington.'

'I thought you said Althorp,' said her husband sharply.

'I did. And it's two Ps.'

'I thought you said –' his wife began, but I stepped in and stopped the fight. I'm always happy to chew the rag with lawyers in pyjamas, but I couldn't hang around all night doing this vaudeville stuff.

'Look, I've said it once and I'll say it again. I'm extremely sorry, but the thing was an accident. All right?'

They looked doubtful.

'You're not suggesting I did this on purpose, are you?'

No, they conceded grimly, they weren't suggesting that.

'Well then. Let's stop talking and ring the police. Pronto.'

'The police?'

'About the burglar.'

'I thought you said it was a pigeon.'

'I said it *may* have been a pigeon.'

'But you said –'

'No, I didn't,' I said sternly. 'Where is your telephone, please?'

The man marched me into the kitchen and I asked if he had a beer – I was pretty thirsty after all the excitement. He looked at me venomously, then fumbled about in the fridge. I picked up the phone and dialled: 9 . . . 9 . . . 8. No answer. Odd. I announced to nobody in particular that there was a cat-burglar on the prowl in w2 and could the old Bill put down their drinks if they had a moment and pop across for a second opinion. My barrister friend handed me a can of Budweiser. From the way his cheeks were puffing out like footballs and molten lava was streaming in rivulets out of his mouth, he was getting seriously pissed off.

'God, you're really gross, aren't you?'

I looked blank. It seemed an odd way to address the deity, but perhaps he was an agnostic.

'You really are one of the grossest, rudest, shittiest men I've ever met in my life.'

He *did* mean me. It takes all sorts. I took a gulp of the Budweiser. Beautiful stuff.

'If you ask me, you're a right bastard.' I didn't ask him, of course, but it's a free country. 'Are you a journalist or something?'

'Oh, something. Definitely.'

'What thing?'

'Not a journalist. Something else.'

'What else?'

'A doctor, since you ask. Ears, nose and throat.'

'Are you seriously telling me –'

'I'd have your sinuses checked if I were you. By the way, you don't have a ham sandwich in that fridge, do you?'

That did him. His mouth dropped open and he started making little gulping movements like a member of the plaice or turbot family who had been overdoing things on a night out. When his wife appeared, all he could do was gesticulate in my direction and tear out his hair in fistfuls. It seemed the diplomatic moment to leave, so I downed the beer, made my apologies to his missus and shimmied out to the street. There was a Mars bar in the glove compartment of my car and I fell on it like a tiger. I get really hungry on these big political assignments.

The next day dawned bright and fresh and clear. The birds were singing across the street from my flat and the bacon and eggs and sausages slipped down like the first whisky at a Burns night party. I was annoyed I'd lost the tape-recorder and I had a bruise the size of a cricket ball from my crash-landing on the bed. But I was winning.

At ten thirty I called Brian at the paper to report progress.

'I've got them stitched up,' I announced proudly. 'Naked

as the day they were born. And there was a cat in on the action, which will amuse our younger readers. When do you want the copy?'

'I don't,' he snapped.

'Come again?'

'I don't want any copy because it's too bloody late. The story's as cold as yesterday's breakfast. Give up and get into work.'

'Chief, I don't understand.'

'You heard me, Beef.'

He hung up and I admit I was shaken. Brian Sparkes may be IQ-negative, but he's a bloody good editor and he can tell the difference between a dead story and a live story faster than a ferret sniffing a rabbit. If he said no dice, it was no dice. I sulked my way through a couple of croissants, then lurched across the road to the newsagent. A banner headline in one of the rival tabloids hit me rudely in the eye. FOXED BY LOVE – The Colonel's Confession. I parted grimly with 20p and started to read.

An astonishing political romance was made public last night when Sir Walter Hockley-Giles MP announced he had separated from his wife Jane and would be living with pretty Opposition MP, Lynn Todd.

Birmingham-based Lynn, a 5'2" brunette, is best known for campaigning for animal rights – an irony not lost on Sir Walter, who is a life-long fox-hunter.

'I've chased my last fox,' laughed 68-year-old Sir Walter. 'But it took a good woman's love to make me see the error of my ways. Lynn's a real lady and we're very happy together.'

Lady Hockley-Giles was not available for comment last night, but it is understood . . .

I let out a low growl and the newsagent looked at me anxiously.

'Are you all right, Mr Wellington?'

'Never felt better. Bit of sausage went down the wrong way.'

I turned to the second page and another headline reared up at me.

DOCTOR DROPS IN

A young London couple had their sleep disturbed in unusual circumstances last night, when an overweight doctor fell through the roof of their bedroom.

'What he was doing up there I'll never know,' said barrister Simon Arbuthnott, 32. 'He was enormous.'

Simon's pretty barrister wife Rosalind agreed. 'The fattest man I've ever seen. He must have weighed...'

I looked blackly at the newsagent.

'Do you always stock this paper?'

'Yes, Mr Wellington.'

'Do people buy it?'

'Some people. Why...?'

'They should be lined up against a wall and shot. Every last one of them.'

I threw the paper to the floor and stormed out. Melodramatic, I know, but a man's got to take a stand on the big issues.

I tracked down H-G in the Strangers Bar, where he and Lynn were standing everyone a round. I suppose, if you're going to come out of the closet with some news which will send your friends and relatives white-haired to the grave, you might as well do it in style; but the whole thing was pretty sordid. Just looking at them together made you realise that nature had done her damnedest to ensure such things didn't happen.

'Congratulations, Walter,' I said, gripping his hand with as much bonhomie as I could muster. 'I never had an inkling. Well done, Lynn. You've made an old man very happy.'

H-G chuckled. I'd known him twenty years and never

45

seen him so chipper about anything. It does that to a man – love, I mean, not the other thing, which generally has the opposite effect.

'What made you finally go public?' I asked him.

'Do you really want to know?'

'Of course.'

He put an avuncular arm round my shoulder and took me out on to the terrace. 'Your lot,' he whispered, when we were out of earshot of the others.

'My lot?'

'Hacks, news-hounds, press busybodies. You won't believe this, Beef, but I had one of them perched outside my bedroom window last night.'

'No.'

'I did. He scarpered and left his tape-recorder behind. A tape-recorder – can you imagine? By a bedroom window.'

'Shocking.'

'No journalist of your generation would do something like that. You might write the most frightful tosh, but you've got professional standards. You're an old pro, Beef.'

'Thanks, Walter, I appreciate that.'

'So what were we supposed to do? At least if we made a clean breast of things, it would spoil the little worm's scoop. You could say . . .' Here a kind of crapulous giggling fit overwhelmed him and he had to lean against the parapet to steady himself. 'You could say . . . we shot his fox!'

I handed him my glass sternly. There was no way I was laughing at that sort of gag.

'Make this one a double, could you, Walter?'

46

3

ROTTWEILER BREATH TEST SHOCK!

I was proceeding in an orderly fashion down Park Lane, keeping a good hundred yards between myself and the car in front, when a siren sounded, a police car roared up to my right and a man with a face not unlike my Aunt Jessica's Rottweiler gestured to me to pull over to the side of the road.

I consulted the speedometer. Twenty-seven miles an hour, top whack. I'd known the old beauty pass fifty in an emergency, but it's generally the sedatest of creatures due to its extreme antiquity. I offered it to a dealer last year, we agreed £25 and he asked if I was paying cash. There had obviously been a misunderstanding. I gave the policeman a cordial wave, accelerated to twenty-nine miles an hour and proceeded on my way.

Bugger me if he didn't carry on signalling to me to stop. There was a purple tinge in his cheeks I didn't like at all. I pulled over, got out of the car and he did the same. We inspected each other. From the way he swayed backwards with his mouth open, I suspect he was used to a leaner class of criminal. But he regained his composure.

'Name?'

I gave the name of the Minister of Transport. It seemed best not to involve the ancient name of Wellington in any unpleasantness. He entered it in his notebook.

'Address?'

I made up somewhere in Maida Vale. I didn't see why the Minister of Transport should be dragged through the courts. This too he wrote down meticulously, asking me to spell 'acacia'. I saw merit in lightening the atmosphere by saying what a nice change it was for a journalist to answer questions while someone else scribbled down the answers in a notebook. I saw demerit. I kept mum.

'Can I see your driving licence, Mr Everard?'

'I'm sorry, officer, I believe I left it at home.'

'Do you have any other form of identification?'

I was ready for that one. Not a sausage, I said smoothly. It was some years since my mother had sewn name-tapes in my underpants and my wallet had been stolen that afternoon in Victoria Street.

He frowned. I don't know if you've seen a Rottweiler frown, but it's a deal more sinister than their usual chirpy grin. The man's inability to distinguish comedy from tragedy was becoming positively oppressive.

'This is no laughing matter, Mr Everard,' he pronounced. Just like that. I'd have argued the point with enthusiasm, but he seemed uninterested in the finer shades of philosophy. He paced moodily round the car, pausing to inspect one of the tyres. I lit a cigarette.

'Do you know why I asked you to stop, Mr Everard?' he enquired, putting a fair dollop of sarcasm into the question.

'I'm sorry, officer, I'm completely at a loss.'

And I was. If everyone drove round London as slowly as me, there would be no need for traffic cops.

'Your lights, Mr Everard.' He pointed an accusing finger. 'They aren't switched on.'

I looked. He was right, sod him. 'How careless of me. And I suppose it's after lighting-up time?'

'Yes, Mr Everard.' He took out his notebook again and gave me a grim look. 'Three o'clock in the morning, Mr Everard.'

'Three o'clock? In the morning?'

I looked around. The streets were deserted and there was,

now he mentioned it, a certain duskiness in the air. I could have sworn it was one thirty in the afternoon, but my theory didn't seem to fit the facts too snugly, so I didn't press it. To be frank, my head was still throbbing after some Burns Night revelry with my Scottish confrères.

I noticed the policeman's nose twitching slightly. He had resembled a Rottweiler out of sorts with the world: he now took on the appearance of a Rottweiler who has smelled uncooked meat. He put his nose close to my mouth and inhaled.

'Can I ask if you've been drinking, Mr Everard?'

'Of course.'

'Of course?'

'Of course you can ask. As many questions as you like. My specialised subject's horse-racing, but I'm pretty well informed on the sex lives of Cabinet Ministers. Fire away.'

His brow darkened. If he was deriving secret pleasure from my banter, he was concealing it consummately.

'*Have* you been drinking, Mr Everard?'

'I suppose yes.'

'You suppose yes.' He noted the fact with satisfaction. 'And how much have you been drinking, Mr Everard?'

'I suppose three glasses.'

'You suppose three glasses.'

'Maybe four glasses. Spread over several hours. Does four glasses sound right?'

Four bottles would have sounded righter, but I didn't want to alarm the good man.

'I wasn't with you, Mr Everard. I wouldn't know.'

'Of course you weren't. Silly of me. I hope I don't need to say that you'd have been most welcome, particularly if you have Scottish blood. We've never excluded policemen from our little gatherings, provided they're out of uniform and don't talk about car insurance. Officer, listen,' I went on hastily, this foray into comedy having fared no better than the previous ones. 'There's something I should tell you.'

I hesitated. One doesn't like to boast and, if one does

49

hold a position of responsibility in society, it's pretty cheap to use it to steal a march on everyone else. But the man's attentions had become so claustrophobic it seemed best to play my trump card sooner rather than later.

'I'm a journalist,' I announced, spreading myself to my full width. 'I work at the House of Commons.'

He snapped his notebook shut. 'You're coming along to the station right now.'

Half an hour later, I was breathing into the old apparatus in the time-honoured way. I was mildly apprehensive, but no more. Burns Night in the Press Bar at the House of Commons is no ordinary revel: Jock journos knock the stuff back as if they're taking a glass of water to swallow a pill and only the best-trained Sassenachs can keep up. On the other hand, the purpose of the breath-test isn't to establish how much someone's drunk but the proportion of alcohol to blood in their bloodstream. A man of my stature doesn't so much have a bloodstream as a blood-river: by the time the hooch has trickled down every artery and made its way to the outlying parts, I'm no worse off than a woman of seven stone who's been sipping lager and lime all evening. And the facts prove it. Six times breathalysed and never nicked. There are Church of England curates who can't boast that sort of record.

Imagine my alarm when the policeman completed his business and grinned. There's only one thing that makes a policeman grin, in my experience, and that's the law being broken into a hundred pieces.

'Do you have a lawyer, Mr Everard? I think you're going to need one.'

'Over the limit, am I?'

'Ten milligrams. Not much, but they always convict. Driving without headlights, driving under the influence . . .' He seemed to be totting up the fine in his head like an accountant.

'Thank you, officer,' I said stiffly. 'If you don't mind, I have a headache and your Judge Jeffreys impersonations are aggravating it. Just pop a letter in the post and I'll send the fiver.'

'It will be more than a fiver, Mr Everard.'

'I can go to ten, but that's my last offer. Can I go now, please?'

I allowed myself a quiet smile in the taxi home. A bit distasteful, the whole experience, but I'd preserved my incognito. I knew they wouldn't be able to trace me through the car because, for reasons I won't go into, it was registered in the name of an aunt who died in 1975. I was safe.

I was struggling to get the key of the front door out of my trouser pocket when a heavy hand descended on my shoulder and I caught the unmistakable whiff of Rottweiler.

'Having trouble, Mr Everard?'

By now he wasn't so much gloating as marching in open triumph over my finer feelings. He stooped to inspect the name over the door-bell, then drew himself up to his full height.

'Or should I say Mr Wellington, Mr Wellington?' The inevitable notebook was produced. 'And I don't think this is Acacia Avenue either, is it? Oh dear, oh dear, oh dear. We're not completely stupid in the force, you know.'

I wondered if this was a good moment to dust off the old joke that, if pigs could fly, Scotland Yard would be the third London airport. On balance I thought better not, but my patience with the man was wearing thin. If he made any more excursions into irony, he was taking his life in his hands.

He licked his lips. It was no good: he simply hadn't grasped the calibre of his antagonist.

'Did I ask if you had a lawyer, Mr Wellington? I'd make that two lawyers if I were you. Let me see, what have we got here?' He consulted his notes. 'Driving a vehicle without headlights, driving a vehicle under the influence of alcohol, giving a false name and address, obstructing the course of justice . . .'

A happy thought struck me. The list had become so encyclopaedic that, if you added 'assaulting a police officer'

51

to the charge sheet, it would pass unnoticed in the general merriment. I picked out a tender-looking spot in his upper groin, swung back my boot and let fly . . .

What with one thing and another, it was several hours before I finally got home. Threats of court appearances, hefty fines and prison sentences were ringing in my ears and, although juries of seven men and five women can be relied on to see the funny side of things faster than policemen, I didn't fancy my chances. I was just mixing an Alka-Seltzer when the telephone rang.

'Mr Wellington?'

'Speaking.'

'This is Mr Hassard's private office.' (Rt Hon Peter Hassard MP, thickest man I've ever met, Cabinet Minister.)

'His private office? In the Ministry?' My nose twitched. Either I was about to be offered the OBE or this was someone's idea of a joke. 'What can I do for you, private office?'

'Mr Hassard has asked me to find out if you would be able to come to lunch on Sunday.'

'I'm sorry, the line's bad. Did you say lunch? This coming Sunday?'

'Mr Hassard wants to brief selected lobby correspondents on an informal basis.'

Everything fell into place. 'I'm with you. He wants to lush up the press and I'm the token representative of the tabloids. Why didn't you say so in the first place? Where's this orgy happening?'

'Maidenhead.'

'Count me in. I have special dietary needs, but if Mrs Hassard could run to leek and potato soup, goulash and dumplings and apple turnover, I'd be grateful. Twelve-thirty for one?'

I turned my car into the Hassards' drive just as Bob Mumford was doing the same. Bob, as you know, writes a column for the heaviest of the Sunday heavyweights: when he sneezes, the whole of Hampstead catches a cold. He greeted me glumly, as if he had been expecting a more exclusive gathering.

'Any idea what this is all about, Beef?'

'Just a PR stunt by the sound of it. He wants to get the press on his side about something.'

'He can't be serious.'

'He's an optimist.'

'He's got to be.'

We exchanged looks. Peter Hassard was one of those one-man disaster areas who wouldn't have the press on his side if he announced a three-day week and made whisky tax-deductible. If he hoped to improve his image by inviting a few journos to his trough and showing them the family photo albums, he was even denser than we thought. Which is saying something.

One of the glories of the Mother of Parliaments is that it contains a hard core of Members who, in an earlier age, would have been exhibited in circuses. And of all the wallies who ever got up on their hind legs and said, 'Mr Speaker, I shall not detain the House', Peter Vossburgh Hassard is in a class of his own. You could write a whole column describing his attempts to speak and stand upright at the same time. I've done it.

When he first arrived in the House, we surmised that there had been an outbreak of mad cow disease among his constituents. When he was made a junior Whip, we assumed it was a device to keep him from making a spectacle of himself on the backbenches. Upon his elevation to Parliamentary Under-Secretary at the Scottish Office, we shook our heads and said, ah well, it's only a few million Jocks. But when he rose to Minister of State at the Department of Employment and from there to the Cabinet, we were genuinely stumped for an explanation. All we could think was that the Prime Minister had inadvertently mistaken him for Peter Hallett – an ageing and talentless dipsomaniac who could at least string together an English sentence and get out of a ministerial car without falling flat on the pavement.

Mind you, he had a Mickey Mouse portfolio: Minister for the Quality of Life. This was a stunt by the Prime Minister, who had realised that quality-of-life issues were flavour of the month, given Hassard a spanking new building on the Embankment and a budget of £300 million and told him to get on with it. Hassard hadn't actually got on with it yet because Ministers take time to master their brief and, as he'd only been in the job eighteen months, barely long enough to master his pencil sharpener, he wasn't expected to do anything in the foreseeable future. But perhaps, Bob and I speculated as we rang the door-bell, he was about to start . . .

The man himself opened the door. 'Very good of you to come, Bob,' he said shaking my hand. 'How are you, Beef?' he continued, giving Bob a welcoming smile. He took our coats, knocked over a hat-stand and stubbed his toe on a set of old golf-clubs. 'The bathroom's this way,' he announced, opening a broom-cupboard from which a cat leapt out. 'Just make yourselves at home.' His shoe got caught under a table and he had to struggle to free himself. 'Why not come through?' There was a hypnotic quality in his clumsiness: you expected his head to fall off his shoulders at any moment.

In the drawing-room, the others had already gathered and were sipping sherry. The cast-list at these informal briefings is always the same: a phalanx of proper journalists and some poor muggins carrying the flag for the tabloids. It's called balance. The Minister holds forth for half an hour and we all write about 'Government sources' and pretend the meeting hasn't happened. It's called investigative journalism.

The only mystery this time was why Hassard had bothered to throw in lunch. If he wanted to show off his clean wholesome family, he should have chosen a different family. The supporting cast was dreadful: a couple of grimy kids throwing mud at each other in the garden and a woman in a tweed skirt dispensing sherry with the air of an early Christian martyr. Something else was obviously afoot . . .

It all came out a few minutes later and pretty nasty it was.

Hassard cleared his throat and clapped his hands. 'If I could have your attention please, gentlemen. I thought that before we got on to the *main* business of the afternoon . . .'

He paused, indicating that laughter was in order. Nobody else laughed, so he laughed himself.

'Far be it from me to keep journalists from their food . . .'

He paused again: again his thin chuckle was the only sound in the room. What you have to keep remembering with this comedian is that 30,000 people voted for him at the last election.

'I thought we'd have this little off-the-record chat to share some of the Government's latest thinking with you. Whatever you boys say in your columns, and I know you have to sell newspapers,' (*chuckle*) 'we're a listening Government' (*chuckle*) 'and our attitude to the press has always been – if you can't beat 'em, join 'em.' (*Double chuckle*) 'Now, before you all ask me questions, I'm going to ask *you* a question.' (*Prolonged and embarrassing chuckle*) 'What do you make of this sherry we're drinking?'

There was a bemused silence, then polite mumbles of approval. I was slow to react or I would have put the record straight immediately: the stuff was the colour of cooking oil and tasted like something vets poured into ailing horses.

Hassard rubbed his hands gleefully. 'I'm glad you approve – because it doesn't have any alcohol in it!' He whipped out a bottle from behind a chair and pointed out the NON-ALCOHOLIC label. 'What about that then?'

The consternation at this announcement was considerable. Serious and tabloid journalists diverge about what constitutes news, but on what constitutes a decent before-lunch drink we are of one mind. A few fellow travellers at the front well-welled and fancy-thatted with frozen smiles on their faces, but the rumblings of mutiny from the back were unmistakable. I started a chant of 'Money back!' and even Bob Mumford joined in.

'No, but seriously,' Hassard went on. 'Seriously. Quite

seriously.' He still had the same goofy smile on his face as when he started: I really don't think he understood the affront he'd given. 'The Government's not insisting that you or anyone else change the habits of a lifetime. No, no, no. We're just saying, think about it. Think about it seriously. You can have a jolly good time without any side-effects at all. That's the message we're keen to get across to the public – and any help you boys can give us would be greatly appreciated. Are there any questions?'

There were. There were indeed. They came from every direction and they came loaded. Most of them began 'Do you seriously . . . ?' and ended with references to men in white coats. If he imagined he could ask a crack team of journalists to Berkshire on a Sunday to endorse a campaign against alcoholism, he imagined wrong. To a man, we put down our glasses and refused to drink another drop. The sense of comradeship in adversity was magnificent. When old Billy Harvey, the chairman of the parliamentary lobby, thundered that, if Ministers deceived the press in this way, the fabric of society was threatened, he spoke for every one of us.

Hassard was looking like a scarecrow which had intercepted a force nine gale when his wife came in and announced that lunch was ready. Questioning was suspended and we trouped through to the dining-room. Feelings were still running high. When I saw the table strewn with salad-bowls and bottles of elderberry wine, it all became too much for me. My head throbbed, my eyes stopped focusing and my knees buckled beneath me. Five minutes later, I was laid out on an upstairs bed with Mrs Hassard bathing my temples with a wet flannel.

The only phase of this man Hassard's parliamentary career which was an unqualified success was the years 1986 to 1988. He didn't put a foot wrong in all that time – mainly because he had lost his seat at the general election and wasn't in the House to make a fool of himself.

But where had he been making a fool of himself? Nobody

knew and he wouldn't tell. It was one of the unsolved mysteries of the post-war House of Commons. He just disappeared from the political map and crawled out of the woodwork two years later at a by-election. What he'd been up to in the intervening period was anyone's guess. If you asked him, he shuffled his feet and muttered something about gaining experience in the real world. There was some embarrassing secret there – and the only reason none of us bothered to get to the bottom of it was that Hassard's whole life was such an uninterrupted cock-up we had plenty of material anyway.

Now that I was actually laid out on the man's bed, however, it seemed negligent not to make a few enquiries. I don't know if you ever find yourself in Cabinet Ministers' bedrooms, but the experience has a remarkable effect on a man of inquisitive mind. Your nose twitches, your imagination races and, if there's anything untoward in one of the cupboards, you're led to it by a kind of magnetic attraction. I remember poking around in the Home Secretary's bedroom during a party conference and unearthing instruments of punishment which wouldn't have been out of place in a medieval torture-chamber. Then there was the occasion of the Filipino *au pair* and the corset . . . But I digress.

Peter Hassard's bedroom, it practically goes without saying, was plastered wall to wall with photographs of Peter Hassard. There was Peter Hassard shaking hands with the Pope, Peter Hassard milking a cow, Peter Hassard opening a supermarket, Peter Hassard addressing a meeting of Japanese businessmen and assorted Peter Hassards in short trousers in school photographs, looking as fatuous then as when he came to man's estate.

'Is that Eton?' I asked Barbara Hassard, who was still by my bedside.

'Harrow.' She gave a wan smile. 'It's the same thing.'

'Best days of his life?'

'He'd go back there if he could.'

'Perpetual schoolboy?'

'Definitely.'

I liked her answers: they carried just the tiniest hint of mutiny. Ministers' wives are like this. They stick doggedly by their husbands' sides for twenty years, smiling and smiling and smiling, then the worm turns, mischief enters their soul and they develop a secret urge to kick over the traces and dance about on tables in Greek restaurants. Catch them in rebellious mood and anything can happen.

The bull question – the one my editor would expect me to ask because it's the one readers would want answered – was obvious. What possessed a normal woman like Barbara Hassard to marry a man who could have faded into the background in any lunatic asylum in the country? Supplementary questions suggested themselves along similar lines. Why didn't she run screaming from the house when she realised she'd drawn the short straw? Was it true that he couldn't put on his own clothes? But I forebore. My dealings with the opposite sex may be bedevilled by problems of comprehension but, in matters of old-fashioned chivalry, I defer to nobody. Besides, it wasn't Barbara Hassard I was interested in, but her old man.

'That meeting with the Japanese trade delegation,' I asked, pointing casually at another picture. 'Was that in 1987?'

'In 1985. It was when Peter was at Employment.'

'Are you sure? I could have sworn I met that same delegation in 1987.'

'It couldn't have been 1987 because Peter wasn't in the House.'

'Of course he wasn't. He had that two-year spell doing something else. What was it again?'

'He was running the unit.'

'The unit. Of course. The unit. Can you remind me what the unit was doing? It's slipped my mind.'

I thought I'd made it, but she hesitated, then shook her head. 'I'm sorry. Peter doesn't like me talking about it.'

'Well, of *course* he doesn't,' I said quickly, giving her hand a sympathetic squeeze. (Ginger Hobbs tells me these sympathetic squeezes work wonders with the right sort of woman.) 'Quite understandable he should be reticent about something like that. If I ran that sort of, uh, unit, I'd be exactly the same. But there's one thing I've learnt in life, Barbara. You don't win any prizes for not talking about things. You've got to stand up and be counted. You've got to be prepared to say, yes, I did such-and-such or I ran such-and-such a unit, but why should I feel ashamed about it? Isn't that right, Barbara?'

'Probably. Probably.'

A look of resignation came over her. She sat lost in thought, then crossed to the window and closed the curtain. I thought my chance had gone, but she suddenly muttered: 'It's only those silly yellow things, for God's sake.'

Silly yellow things? The possibilities were endless. I was about to move in with some tough talking and sympathetic squeezes when her noodle of a husband put his head round the door.

'Can you come, darling? It's time for the fruit salad.'

I was minded to comment that a man who'd been to Harrow, milked cows, chinwagged with the Pope and held Japanese businessmen spellbound should be capable of dishing out fruit salad single-handedly. But the Hassards obviously worked as a team. They tripped off downstairs together, leaving me prone on their nuptial bed with a riddle about silly yellow things revolving in my head.

It was nearly two weeks before I cracked it. I was lunching at a new Italian restaurant in Victoria Street, sampling the *scallopino alla marsala* and watching the world go by, when my eye was caught by a piece of street theatre across the road, involving a Ford Sierra and a woman in a beige rain-coat with a sense of humour failure. I had one of my intuit-ive flashes and knew all. Pausing only to pay my respects to the sweet trolley, I took a taxi to the House and got on the telephone. Half an hour later, it was a dapper and quietly confident Beef who knocked on the door of the Rt Hon Peter Hassard MP.

My private affairs in the last two weeks hadn't been going

well. A letter had arrived requiring my presence in court on five charges and, when I showed it to Nigel 'Bender' Marsh, my solicitor, his face went very black. From my days as a cub reporter at the Midsomer Norton magistrates court, I assumed all that was needed was to get a decent lawyer, get the lawyer to say rude things about the policeman's mother and the bench would come out in favour of the little man. But Bender was having none of it.

'Beef, there's no way you can play the little man.'

'You don't have to be personal, Bender.'

'I'm not talking weight, I'm talking law. Have one over the eight and, so long as it's only one, the bench will be on your side. They've all done it themselves. But kick a policeman in the balls and you're touching a raw nerve. It's no good, Beef. Unless you can prove the whole thing was an accident –'

'They'll never swallow that. As soon as they set eyes on this Rottweiler, they'll know I did it on purpose with music in my heart. Can't I plead provocation?'

'Did he hit you?'

'He made four bad jokes running. He was a horror.'

'I wish you luck,' said Bender gloomily. 'But if I were you, I'd cancel my summer holiday and take out an extension on the mortgage.'

It was to avert such indignities that I'd come to see Peter Hassard. I found him sitting at his desk bent forward struggling to do up his shoe-laces. A coffee-stain down the front of his shirt and a rip in the armpit of his jacket indicated that he was enjoying a normal day. He greeted me with a cheery wave, knocking over a carafe of water.

'This is a surprise, Beef. Keeping well?'

'Yes, thank you.'

'That was a nasty turn you took the other day. I hope we didn't poison you?'

'Not at all.'

'Good. Excellent. Between ourselves, I'm glad to see a newspaper man right now. We're about to launch a new publicity campaign and I'd be interested to see what you made of it. Here, have a look.'

He rummaged behind his desk and, with a theatrical flourish, produced a poster of a white policeman patting a black schoolgirl on the head under the legend FRIENDS. The montage puzzled me.

'Are you cracking down on child abuse?'

'Don't make mischief. You know perfectly well what it is.'

'Peter, I'm foxed. Was it a film you saw? Does South Africa come into it? Is it a new poetry competition?'

'I do wish you'd be serious,' he grumbled. 'No wonder the country's in such a mess if the press won't support the Government. Read this.'

He passed me a press hand-out, embargoed till the following day. I read it in stunned silence, with a tickling sensation at the back of my throat.

Rt Hon Peter Hassard, Minister for the Quality of Life, today launched a major campaign to improve relations between the police and the community.

He said: 'We must do everything in our power to revive the sense of trust and affection which ordinary people used to feel for the bobby on the beat. My Ministry has already promoted non-alcoholic drinks as one means of reducing crimes of violence. We shall now focus attention on the need for everyone in the community to co-operate with the police in maintaining law and order.'

'Strong stuff, isn't it?' he chirruped. 'I've got a million posters done for less than £300,000. It all goes to show that you don't need to chuck money at problems to solve them. You just need to use your imagination and capture people's hearts and minds. We're reviewing sentencing policy as well. If anyone tries —'

'Don't tell me', I shuddered. 'In Hassard's brave new world, any poor mixed-up kid who gets sloshed and takes a swing at a copper is going to be trudging round Dartmoor in pyjamas for twenty years with a ball and chain round his leg. And I dare say,' I added, opening his fridge on the off-chance he had some Scotch, 'that a mixed-up adult won't fare any better. It stinks, Peter.'

'You don't like it?'

'I do not. I've heard better proposals from bearded Cypriots in caftans addressing two men and a dog at Speakers Corner on a Sunday morning. There was a mad professor in one of the *Carry On* films who believed – but enough badinage. I haven't come to talk about your crackpot schemes. I have a sterner purpose. I know,' I said, with a touch of subtle menace in my manly baritone, 'about the unit.'

The effect of these words was remarkable. Hassard had been leaning against the mantelpiece with the air of a man who might not know his two-times table but could swop pleasantries with the best. He now jumped six inches in the air, clutched his brow, let out a yelp of horror, turned the colour of a newly painted London bus and stumbled backwards into the fireplace. His next line lacked conviction in the circumstances.

'I don't know what you're talking about.'

'Of course you do. That unit you ran between 1986 and 1988. I have all the facts.'

'You don't.'

'I do.'

'You don't, damn you.'

I held up my hand. 'Peter, please. It is two thirty. At five past three a horse is running at Wincanton with my shirt on its back. Let's get down to business. Tomorrow morning, subject to certain assurances from you, my paper will carry the whole story. Provisional headline – THE MINISTER AND THE LITTLE YELLOW THINGS.'

He staggered.

'Beef, you can't.'

'I can and I will. I shall relate in my purplest prose how intuition and determination led me relentlessly to one of the secrets of the century. I shall relate how, between June 1986 and February 1988, you ran a cowboy wheel-clamping unit in West Kensington. I shall relate how you and your fellow mobsters drove round the metropolis with a van-load of yellow clamps looking for illegally parked vehicles. I shall relate how you clamped the vehicles, charged £50 to unclamp them, gave the police £17.50 and pocketed the change. I shall –'

'It was perfectly legal, Beef.'

'No doubt. But that isn't the point. It's what the man in the polling-booth thinks that matters. With the possible exception of snooker players and management consultants, wheel-clampers are the most despised profession in London. They have spoiled more people's day out in town than the Tate Gallery and Madame Tussaud's put together. When people find out that a Cabinet Minister's been in on the racket, the backlash will be brutal. I'm sorry, Peter, but you're for it.'

By now the poor man's condition could only be called abject. He sat in a crumpled heap with his head in his hands, looking like a man whose house had been blown away in a hurricane with his wife and children and underpants inside it. I've seen more moral fibre in a Sainsbury's rice pudding.

'You said something about assurances,' he stuttered. 'Me making certain assurances.'

'I did. That's what I came to talk about. Basically, my friend, if you give me the assurances, the story won't be printed and your secret will be safe. My word as a journalist.'

'What sort of assurances?'

'There are two. First, go easy on this quality of life stuff. The campaign for non-alcoholic drinks must stop. Before you know it, there'll be NO ALCOHOL areas in pubs and the state will totter. And I don't like that poster. Burn it.'

'Burn –? But we've printed a million.'

'Burn the lot. The Treasury will stump up: it's called nugatory expenditure. I've nothing against West Indian girls in school uniform but, at this point in my life, I'm not prepared to see policemen looking like St Francis of Assisi photographed in soft focus against a background of swans and tulips. It's tasteless and far-fetched – which brings me to my second point. Next Tuesday, the case of Regina versus Wellington is due to be heard at Horseferry Road magistrates court.'

He scratched his ear.

'Wellington? Of course, that's you. What was the other name?'

'I'll write it down for you. The point is that this trial must not proceed. Counsel for the prosecution must stand up and announce that all charges against me are to be dropped. He must apologise in open court for the slur cast on my character –'

'I don't follow.'

'– and, as well as recommending that costs be awarded in my favour, he must tell the court that the police officer in the case has been reprimanded for harassing a sober and law-abiding member of the public. Have you got all that?'

My meaning took between three and four minutes to percolate through to the Hassard think-tank but, when it did, the effect was electric. His mouth dropped open, his lips quivered and his eyes popped in their sockets as if some nameless horror from outer space had crawled out of the fireplace.

'Beef, it's out of the question. We've got an independent justiciary. It would a flagrant abuse of the legal system.'

'The word's judiciary and we don't. Systems are run by human beings and anything run by human beings can be monkeyed about with. One of the pleasures of recuperating in your bedroom last month, Peter, was the opportunity to study a group of spotty schoolkids in white trousers –'

'The Harrow third XI?'

'If you say so. It looked more like the seventh to me: I've never seen such a shower. Sitting next to you in the front row with his knees crossed, holding a cricket bat the wrong way up and looking like the boy that time forgot –'

'Buns Corrigan?'

64

'Sir Jeremy Corrigan, Director of Public Prosecutions. A quiet word from you in his ear and events at Horseferry Road next week will proceed exactly as I have described. Tell him a valued friend of yours is about to become the victim of a gross miscarriage of justice and –'

'I can't say that.'

'Of course you can. Fill your mind with what will happen if your constituents find out you used to play silly buggers with wheel-clamps, and you'll say it with gusto.'

He looked doubtful, then a thought struck him.

'Beef, we did open the batting together.'

'There you are then.'

'We were really quite good chums. I remember we put on forty-three against Radley on an absolute pig of a wicket. In the first two overs alone –'

I rose to leave. 'Another time, if you don't mind, Peter. They'll be coming under starter's orders at Wincanton. Just get on the telephone and do the necessary, could you?'

4

CHANCELLOR QUITS!

Within minutes of shaking hands with Sebastian Carr, I
had taken a violent dislike to the little pimple. He was
wearing a Paisley tie, which I was willing to overlook, and
he was carrying a copy of *The Economist*, which I put down
to youthful high spirits. But there was something fresh and
keen and coltish in his manner which went through me like
a plate of prunes.

'What will you have, Seb?' I asked cordially, enthroned
on my stool in the Press Bar, where the more studious
members of the lobby were mustering for a mid-morning
drink.

'A half of lager please, Beef.'

I nearly dropped my bacon sandwich into the ice-bucket.
It wasn't quite as bad as the time Taff Evans's girlfriend
asked for an orange juice and the barman had to go on a
foray down Victoria Street, but it came a close second.
These half-of-lager merchants are the scourge of the drinking classes: everyone else has unbuttoned nicely and they
are still talking about the weather and where they went on
their summer holiday. What a semi-teetotal milksop was
doing in my line of business had me completely foxed.

'So,' he said, looking saucer-eyed around the bar. 'This
is it.'

There was no obvious answer to that one, so I ordered
another bacon sandwich.

'Where the action takes place,' he added, with hushed reverence.

I followed his gaze. The only other people in the bar were some BBC groupies, the textiles correspondent of the *Financial Times*, a Hansard reporter with a secret sorrow and an assortment of clapped-out gypsies from the regional press. A serious misunderstanding seemed to have arisen.

'Which are the MPs?' he whispered. 'I'd love to be introduced.'

I saw that stern words were needed. 'There aren't any. This is the Press Bar.'

'Oh.' He blushed prettily. 'But I thought MPs and lobby correspondents drank together and that's how –'

'No.'

'But I thought –'

'No. If we're desperate for news, and we're not because it's the football season, we go down to Annie's or the Strangers and grub around for it there. If we just want a civilised drink in civilised company, we have it here. There's a better selection of whiskies,' I added, not feeling I was coming across very well.

He sipped mournfully at his lager. 'I can see there's more to being a lobby correspondent than I thought.'

'There is,' I agreed, with dark emphasis. 'I could have told you that before you got here.'

I wonder if you've noticed how, in the dialogue quoted, I'm less than my chummy self? Well, I was feeling less than my chummy self, and I'll tell you why.

This little pimple, this fresh-faced, wide-eyed, lager-sipper, was no ordinary wet-behind-the-ears apprentice learning the ropes on his first day at work. He was a traitor to his profession and a self-confessed enemy spy. Only a man of warmth and magnanimity would have bought the little excrescence his lager.

His official title was assistant to the parliamentary correspondent, i.e. my sidekick. If his duties had been confined to sharpening my pencil and pushing me round in

68

a wheelchair from one bar to another, I would have given him a hearty welcome. But his real function was more sinister. He was there because Brian Sparkes, my editor, no longer trusted me to do the job on my own: he wanted someone to cover for me on what he called my 'off days'. And I'll tell you something. When you're no longer trusted to do a job which involves keeping your ears in the pricked position and sitting on a bar-stool till closing time without falling off, it really gets up your nose.

The other villain of the piece was the new Chancellor of the Exchequer, one Gordon Spade, a self-important man with a warped sense of humour. When he announced that he would break with tradition and deliver his first Budget on a Thursday, the same day as the Cheltenham Gold Cup, the Press Gallery erupted like the wailing wall in Jerusalem. Fair enough if the man had realised his error and made a prompt apology. We old journos are forgiving souls: we cock a leg, then move on to the next tree. But he just stuck to his guns, said he didn't see why the management of the economy should be influenced by such frivolous considerations and wasn't changing the date for love or money. I despair of humanity sometimes.

You can probably guess the rest. The correspondents of the heavies gritted their teeth, stayed at Westminster and watched the race on television. The rest of us went to Cheltenham and watched the Budget on television. A perfectly reasonable compromise, I'm sure you'll agree. It was only when some smart-arsed cameraman spotted me next to the winners' enclosure and did a fancy panning shot from one side of my stomach to the other that the thing came unstuck. Next morning came the inevitable summons to the editor's office. How, he asked tartly, had I known that backbenchers' reaction to the Budget had been mixed when I'd been a hundred miles away? Very simple, I retorted. Because backbenchers' reaction to Budgets was always mixed. It had been mixed since God made the birds and the bees. Show me two backbenchers, I said, and I will show you a mixed reaction. He dismissed me with a growl and I thought I had got the better of the exchange. Then, two days later, came the news that I was to be given an assistant . . .

The bells rang to signal the start of the afternoon sitting and Sebastian shot to his feet.

'Aren't you coming, Beef?'

'Is there a fire drill?'

'To Questions. It's Health and Social Security. There may be something on the nurses' strike.'

I looked at him stupefied. It was his first day at work, but even so . . . I couldn't credit that a paid-up member of the National Union of Journalists could be so naïve. The idea that a Government Minister should say something in the House of Commons worth reporting in the tabloid press belonged in the realms of medieval witchcraft.

'I may drop in later,' I said, ordering another drink. 'You go and see what's happening.'

He trotted off cheerfully. I even have a recollection he was humming a snatch from Italian opera.

'New boy?' asked White Walker from the *Mercury*, an old campaigner like myself.

'Fresh from the cabbage-patch this morning,' I said, shaking my head. 'I don't know where they find them. White, is it me or has the younger generation lost its grip? You and I were never that bad, were we?'

'You did once sit through a debate on the Common Fisheries Policy.'

'That was to win a bet with Ginger Hobbs. I didn't write about it afterwards. I didn't fool myself it was news. That boy has gone into the Gallery because he thinks – mark this, White – he seriously thinks that's where the action is. Quite incredible.'

'He'll learn, Beef.'

'But will he?' I asked morosely. 'Will he? If you ask me, he's got Peter Pan written all over him. What are you drinking, White?'

*

Two more weeks with Sebastian as my assistant and I had lost nearly half a stone in weight. My jacket hung limply from my shoulders. My cardigan met in the middle. My trousers barely stayed up at all. Friends passed me in the corridor and muttered: 'He's wasting away. Not long now. Let's have lunch after the memorial service.' I can't remember feeling so miserable.

It was his sheer keenness which did for me. Boyish enthusiasm I can take: I was a boyish enthusiast myself before the gout set in. But this was religious zealotry. He wanted to meet everyone, see everything, go everywhere. He phoned copy through to the paper night and day, pages and pages of the stuff. They didn't print it, of course; but when I tried explaining that it hadn't been printed because it wasn't news, he got attacks of the vapours and launched into long philosophical arguments about what was news and what wasn't news. And he *still* drank halves of lager. I've known people chucked out of the NUJ for less.

And some of the words he used. 'Intransigent.' 'Realignment.' 'Methodology.' I'm sure they're in the dictionary somewhere, but they aren't our house style: if you try playing silly buggers with the plumber's mates in Billericay who form the backbone of our readership, they read something else. On one occasion I had to tear the receiver from his hand to stop him filing an article on the New Butskellism. I reasoned with him. I pleaded with him. I told him about the young deputy foreign editor who'd used the word 'perestroika' in a front-page story and now slept under Charing Cross bridge, but to no avail. I was dealing with a certified intellectual.

Out in the real world, the three-month nurses' strike dragged on and there was no prospect of a settlement. The new Prime Minister was as cunning as the serpent and had formed his Cabinet on the classic principle of creative tension. The Chancellor of the Exchequer, the aforementioned Spade, was a stony-hearted bastard who wasn't going to untrouser a penny unless someone put a gun to his head. The Health Secretary, John Feather, was a walking saint, dripping goodwill and compassion like honey from a spoon. They were said to fight like cats behind the scenes, but in public they formed a united front. Naturally, went the official line, there was nothing the Government would like more than to give the nurses £30,000 a year and remunerate their sterling service to the community; at the same time it would be sheer recklessness, with interest rates and inflation rising, to offer more than a fiver a week plus a uniform allowance. The nurses didn't buy it. The public didn't buy it. But the backbenchers bought it like pet lambs and that was what mattered.

The other point at issue was whether Feather should negotiate with the nurses face to face. They said yes, he said no and some poor sod in the NHS ferried between the two parties like a bookie's runner. Complete deadlock.

Then, out of the blue on a Sunday afternoon, the whole thing blew up in the Government's face. Feather was interviewed on *The World at One* and said that the Government's negotiating position was flexible; half an hour later Spade was interviewed for a different programme and said that anyone who thought the Government's negotiating position was flexible was dangerously deluded. Well, you don't need a master's degree in political science to spot a cock-up on that scale. I remember pausing in the middle of lunch, licking my lips and thinking life in this vale of tears wasn't so bad. CABINET SPLIT is always a good page-filler for a Monday, but you usually have to make up the story to go with the headline. When Ministers are throwing the brown stuff at each other in broad daylight, it saves effort all round.

Five minutes later Sebastian was on the phone, breathing heavily with excitement. 'Did you hear, Beef?'

Yes, I growled, I had heard, did he think I was deaf? A steaming bowl of rhubarb crumble and custard was awaiting my attention, which aggravated my impatience.

'What do you make of it?'

'How should I know? One of them was probably pissed.'

'Do you think the Government's going to give in?'

'Ask a bookmaker.'

'And whose side is the Prime Minister on? If he backs Spade, he'll leave Feather exposed. And if he backs Feather, Spade will look as if he's the one who's out of step. He can't just sit on the fence because it will only make things worse. It's rather exciting, isn't it?'

I forebore to comment. We Wellingtons relish sarcasm and aren't above using it to pulverise lesser mortals into submission. But we have our compassionate side. If the boy wanted to get excited, who was I –

'Have you been ringing round?' he asked eagerly.

'Ringing who?'

'Getting people's reaction to the interviews. The Government side of the House is bound to be split, so we should get some good quotes there. The Opposition will be cock-a-hoop. And we could find out what the nurses have to say. Then if we spoke to someone on the NHS Board of Management –'

'Steady on, Sebastian. One thing at a time.'

I ran my hand over my temples to alleviate a slight throbbing sensation. It's no laughing matter talking to someone who's lost contact with the real world. I was reminded of the time my Uncle Jim finally went off his trolley and ran down Workington High Street in his longjohns singing 'Where Are the Simple Joys of Maidenhood?'

'Isn't there something you're forgetting?' I asked gently, hoping to coax him back into the land of the living. 'It is Sunday afternoon. The nation is at peace. Old men are asleep in armchairs. Middle-aged men are digesting roast beef and Yorkshire pudding. Young men are playing with their computers. Women are in the kitchen doing the washing-up. There is calm. There is order. There is contentment. At five minutes past three, a man in black shorts will blow a whistle and Manchester United football team –'

'It is a big story, Beef,' he grumbled. 'The other papers will go to town on it.'

I saw I hadn't made myself clear. 'My dear young friend, how often do I have to tell you this? We are not other papers. We are a photo album of the Royal Family and a football results service. We investigate forthcoming divorces in the theatrical profession. We provide titillation for dirty men in raincoats who can't afford *Playboy*. But politics we handle with a light touch. If the Government gets itself arse about face, we note the fact on page four. But we don't ring every Tom, Dick and Harry on a Sunday afternoon and ask them what they think about something the Chancellor of the Exchequer's said. It's not on, Sebastian. There's a standard way of covering this sort of story and it's time you learnt it. Do you have a pen?'

'Yes.'

'Then take this down. You watch the six thirty news on BBC and make a note of the facts. You summarise them in four sentences not longer than ten words each. You then ring Jenkins.'

'Jenkins?'

'Paul Jenkins. Member for Birmingham South. You ask him for a short comment on the situation, again no more than ten words. Prefacing his remarks with the phrase, "According to senior backbencher Paul Jenkins", you –'

'He's only been in the House three years.'

'All right then. "Influential backbencher."'

'But he's a complete nobody.'

'Have it your way, Sebastian. "Short-arsed nobody Paul Jenkins, three years in the Commons doing sweet f.a. and the most insignificant twerp to crawl out of the woodwork since Mahatma Gandhi's hairdresser." I think you'll find my version's pithier. Now can I get on with my lunch please? The match is starting in ten minutes.'

I hung up and tottered back to the kitchen. There was something so debilitating about Sebastian: it was like teaching a dyslexic child. I picked listlessly at my rhubarb and as nearly as dammit forgot to have a second helping.

Imagine my emotions when I opened the paper the next morning, turned to page four and saw that he had followed my instructions to the letter. The ten-word sentences, the senior backbencher routine, the works. I could have written the piece myself. It was like the sun coming up over the horizon.

I don't always show this side of my character to best advantage, but I'm a very fair-minded man. Slow to chide and swift to bless: that's Beef to a T. And when Sebastian showed up in the bar at lunchtime, I gave him such a dose of the prodigal son treatment you could practically smell the fatted calf cooking off-stage.

'Well done, lad,' I said, gripping his hand. 'Well done indeed. As fine a piece of journalism as I've read this year. You'll be a lobby correspondent yet. Lay off that lager muck and have a proper drink. I'm really proud of you. Two triples when you're ready, Reg.'

'Thank you,' he said in a dazed voice. 'I was only doing what you told me.'

'And where's the harm in that? You're a young lad. You've got a lot to learn from an old stager like me. We're going to get on famously. Now what's on the agenda this afternoon?'

He looked down at the carpet. 'I thought I might go along to the Treasury Committee.'

'The who?'

'The Treasury Committee.'

'Sebastian, you must forgive an old man's hearing problems. Did you just say the Treasury Committee?'

'Yes. They are taking evidence from the Chancellor at half past four on the Public Expenditure White Paper. Yesterday's interview is bound to come up.'

The smile froze on my lips. I think it was the sheer ingratitude which hurt. I'd dragged him up by the boot-straps and knocked some of the nonsense out of him and there he was back to his bad old ways as if I'd never existed.

'Do you seriously imagine,' I asked slowly, fighting to keep my temper, 'that our readers give a monkey's what the Chancellor tells the Treasury Committee or any other bloody committee? We're here to provide a news service, not write Volume XXII of the History of Parliament. We do sometimes quote what Ministers say on television. We occasionally make reference to what they say in the House. But select committees are for the birds. For Christ's sake, Sebastian. There are dozens of those things and most of them meet at ten thirty in the morning. I expressly forbid –'

'I'm only going along for the atmosphere, Beef. The public's right behind the nurses, so the Chancellor will get a roasting.'

'Have it your way,' I said stiffly. 'But I'm disappointed in you. I thought you were starting to learn the ropes and you're pissing about like a school-leaver covering a church fête. It will end in tears, Sebastian.'

I get the feeling that, if I carry on in this vein, your sympathies will start to waver between the hero and the villain and the moral of the story will go down the tubes. Steady on, Beef, I hear you saying, the boy can't be that bad. Why shouldn't he go and watch the Chancellor being questioned by the Treasury Committee about the nurses' strike?

In the matter of the boy, I make no concessions. He was a pimple and pimples have to be squeezed from time to time. If you'd had to sit and watch him drinking as many halves of lager as I had, you'd find my patience almost saint-like.

In the matter of the nurses, I admit the charge. When stories involving young women in uniform are going begging, no journalist worth his salt is hanging around in bars. I've always had a soft spot for nurses – ever since I was admitted to St Thomas's with a suspected wasting disease and a little Liverpudlian girl with ginger hair ran daily errands to the off-licence – and up to now I'd stood four-square behind them. I'd made a painstaking analysis of the issues on February 11th, under the headline GIVE 'EM THE MONEY, and my follow-up pieces on February 22nd (THE POOR LITTLE ANGELS) and March 7th (COUGH UP, FATSO!) had maintained the theme. So why wasn't I still in there fighting for them?

The truth is that I was and that, beneath my lethargic exterior, the old journalist's juices were working overtime.

Ever since Feather and Spade had made such an almighty balls-up of those interviews, I'd been pummelling my brains how to get to the bottom of the story. And I'd finally cracked it. As Sebastian trotted off to the select committee hearing, I slipped out of the bar and took the lift to the ground floor.

There's a small room just off Speaker's Court where Ministers' drivers congregate while their charges are in the House. It's one of those tough joints you can only penetrate if you have iron in your soul but, once inside the holy of holies, the gossip just flies around. I fought my way through the smoke, paused respectfully as a tense point was reached in the poker game and tracked down Ben Bromage in the far corner. He was smoking a cigarette and studying the visual material on page three of my paper. He looked up with a grin.

'Wotcha, Beef. How are you keeping?'

'Not so bad, Ben. Off my food since Christmas, but I should pull through. Time for a quick one?'

'I can't, Beef. I'm on duty.'

'How long do you have to wait here?'

'Till half five. But you know how it is, Beef.' He grinned again and tapped the side of his nose with his finger. 'If you're the Health Secretary's driver, you can't be seen in uniform down the boozer. Use your common.'

'Come and have a cup of tea then.'

'I didn't think you touched that muck.'

'For a friend like you,' I said, taking him smoothly by the arm, 'I can make an exception.'

Apart from being in the right place at the right time as far as I was concerned, Ben Bromage is as upright a citizen as you'll meet. Kind, decent, straightforward, generous to a fault. I remember him tipping me off that he'd driven the Agriculture Minister to an address in Mayfair incompatible with his married status and asking only £200 for the info. As honest as butter. They say it's the pay that accounts for the calibre of people in the public service, but you should never underestimate that old-fashioned British pride in a day's work well done.

77

'Taken the old man anywhere interesting lately?' I asked, getting down to business.

'He's not still seeing that bird in Camden Lock, if that's what you're after.'

'No, we've done her. I'm talking politics, Ben, I'm talking nurses. Any dirt? Any buzz? Any angle?'

'Not a sausage, Beef. Sorry.'

'You're sure?'

'Sure I'm sure.' He dipped a biscuit into his tea and munched it. A gleam appeared in his eyes. 'No, hang about, there was something. Last Saturday I had to take him to a Chinese restaurant for lunch. On Wardour Street. Two and a half hours he was in there. I remember thinking, hang about, the old man doesn't normally go for Chinky, so what's keeping him?'

I pondered. Eating Chinese wasn't an offence under the Sexual Offences Act, so it fell outside the normal ambit of our readership. But Saturday was the day before Sunday and on Sunday Feather had had that spectacular bust-up with the Chancellor. Perhaps there was something in the beansprouts . . .

'Thanks, Ben,' I said. 'That's helpful. Wardour Street, you said?'

'Number sixty-five. The Green Dragon or the Yellow Peril, something like that. Big place, you can't miss it.'

'Good lad. I've been feeling like a bit of Chinese. I must check it out.' I took out my wallet smoothly. 'Twenty do?'

'I've been a bit short lately, Beef.'

'Forty?'

'Great.'

I counted it out in fivers and handed it across the table. I always pay cash: I'm against cheque-book journalism on principle.

'Hang about, Beef,' he hissed. 'Do you have to be so bleeding obvious? The old Bill's over there.'

I looked where he was pointing. It was my old friend PC Dicky Dodds, no less, having a quiet cup of tea and doing the crossword.

'Don't worry yourself,' I said, getting to my feet. 'I pay him in tenners.'

I ran a cursory eye over the Green Dragon's menu.

'A number eleven, two number eighteens and numbers twenty-four, twenty-seven, thirty-one, thirty-three, and thirty-six to forty-two inclusive, please.'

The waiter paled. 'Are you waiting for someone, sir?'

'No, I'm on my own. Bung in a couple of spring rolls, could you? And a bottle of something French with a bit of body? Good man.'

I lit a cigarette and studied the evening paper. There was a photograph of Feather and Spade on the front page under the headline NURSES: MORE CONFUSION. Both Ministers had been backtracking furiously. Feather was now quoted as saying that the Government's position wasn't entirely flexible, Spade that it wasn't entirely inflexible. It sounded as flexible as a donkey's tail to me, but I'm only a journalist, I don't understand high politics.

I summoned the head waiter. 'Can I have a word, Mr Wang?'

'Wong.'

'I'm sorry. Wong. You looked like a Wang from a distance. It must have been a trick of the light. This man,' I said, pointing at Feather's picture in the paper. 'One of your customers, I believe? Is it true that he's very fond of your shark fin's soup?'

Wong beamed. 'Yes, sir. He likes our shark's fin soup very much.'

'I don't blame him. It's superb. Those sharks haven't died in vain. My compliments to the harpoonist. Did he have some on Saturday?'

'Yes, sir.'

'Which table did he sit at?'

'We've got a private room upst –' He faltered and looked at me. 'You're not press, are you?'

'A journalist? Good God, no!' I threw my head back,

79

rocked to and fro on my chair and laughed till the tears ran down my cheeks. Not easy when you've got a mouthful of chow mein, but it seemed to do the trick.

'He was with a party,' Wong went on. 'They all had the soup.'

'Big party?'

'Four ladies, one gentleman.'

'Ladies? Plural? These politicians really put the boat out, don't they?' I winked. 'They all kept their clothes on, I suppose, Mr Wong? You didn't, by any chance, did you, come across any items of female underwear as you were clearing away the shark's fins?'

'No, sir.'

'Pity.'

There was a frosty silence. My modest suggestion had shocked Wong to the core. I've noticed this before, incidentally. English humour doesn't travel much further than Belgium: by the time you get East of Suez, it's regarded as positively tasteless. And I dare say Chinese jokes don't fare much better coming in the opposite direction.

'So you don't know who those people were with Feather?'

'No, sir.'

'Never seen them before?'

'No, sir.'

'Nothing unusual or distinctive about them?'

'No, sir.'

And that, I thought, was that. Wong was looking po-faced and, if he did know anything, which I doubted, wasn't going to spill. The only thing going for me was my magnificent, eye-catching constitution. I was dispatching so much food with such gusto – shifting from the braised duck to the prawns and from the spoon to the chopsticks with an adroitness you just don't see nowadays – that Wong lingered by my table like a man transfixed. I doubt if he'd seen such artistry since his ship docked at Tilbury in the Sixties. At one particularly neat piece of work with a pancake, his mouth dropped open in sheer admiration – and suddenly we had a conversation again.

'I think,' he murmured, 'that one of the ladies was a nurse.'

'A what?'

'A nurse.'

'Did you say *nurse*?' I spluttered, disgorging nearly half a duck.

'Yes, sir. One of the other customers fainted and she came and helped look after him till the ambulance came.'

'My dear Mr Wong,' I said, quivering with excitement, 'I really think this is the finest restaurant in London.'

'Thank you, sir.'

'I haven't enjoyed myself so much since, since –'

And knock me over with a beansprout, but who should walk through the door that very minute but Tom Hazard? When I tell you that Tom is the Prime Minister's assistant press secretary, and that Wong greeted him with the immortal words, 'Good afternoon, Mr Hazard sir. I hope Saturday's arrangements were satisfactory', you will appreciate my emotions. Quivering with excitement wasn't in it. I wobbled with excitement.

Tom recognised me and pulled a face. 'Beef,' he said glumly. 'What are you doing here?'

'What does it look as if I'm doing?' I retorted, waving a lordly hand at the fodder. 'Cleaning the car? I may need help with that duck. Would you care to join me?'

'Thanks, I'm meeting someone.'

'Not another nurse by any chance?'

He winced. 'I don't know what you're talking about.'

'You will, Tom,' I gloated, pronging a couple of prawns. 'You will. Just read my paper tomorrow morning.'

I squeezed into a call-box in Gerrard Street and got through to the editor. You don't say, 'Hold the front page' on my rag because it's reserved for the Royal Family, but I said, 'Hold page four,' and it went down a treat.

'Something big, Beef?'

'Enormous. Makes Pearl Harbor look like a third division friendly.'

'Let's have it.'

'PM BACKS FEATHER. HEALTH MINISTER IN SECRET TALKS WITH NURSES.'

'What did you say?'

'Those are what we call headlines. They come at the top of the page.'

'Beef, are you pissed?'

'Drunk as a lord. But you'd better believe me because this is the goods. Got a pencil, old cock? "Health Minister John Feather has held secret talks with the nurses – with the full backing of the Prime Minister. Feather met the striking nurses at a Chinese restaurant in Soho last Saturday. They negotiated face to face over shark's fin soup and –."'

'Is this kosher, Beef?'

'As the Ten Commandments. Ask Wong.'

'Wong?'

'The head waiter. Tom Hazard was in on the act too. I saw him with my own eyes. The whole thing's watertight.'

'You've really checked it out?'

'Chief, who do you think I am? Our biggest bloody scoop in years and you're playing footsy-footsy. I had some of the shark's fin soup myself,' I added, resenting the slur on my professionalism.

I took a taxi back to the House and went up to the Press Bar. I remember Winston once coming up with a good one in Annie's about in victory, magnanimity. But, as I told him at the time, he was overstating the case. When you've stuffed your rivals and are sitting on a scoop which is going to make them look pretty bloody silly, you don't waste time being magnanimous. You gloat.

Much to my chagrin, there was nobody to gloat over. The place was a desert: Reg was washing glasses behind the bar, there was a pigeon perched on the window-sill and that was it. I consulted my watch. Five fifteen: standing room only on a normal day. I was baffled. The last race at Chepstow had finished nearly an hour ago.

'Is there a fire drill, Reg?' I asked when he'd lined me up a double.

'No, Beef.'

'You're not on strike, are you?'

'No way.'

'Then what's up? Has the Queen died? Are there nuclear missiles bound for these shores? What are all these empty chairs? I don't like it, Reg.'

'Perhaps there was a row in the House,' he suggested.

'What sort of row?'

'Search me.'

I was considering going to investigate when Sebastian burst through the door. His hair was all over the place, as if he'd been running.

'There you are, Beef. I've been looking for you all afternoon. Where have you been?'

'Eating beansprouts.'

'Are you joking? The Chancellor –'

I held up an imperious hand. 'Stop right there, Sebastian. You are no doubt going to give me a blow by blow account of the Chancellor's appearance before the Treasury Committee. I don't want to know. There are days when I can take tales of derring-do from the Committee Corridor and days when I can't.'

'But, Beef –'

'Don't argue. You're about to get a lesson in the art of journalism which you'll remember all your adult life, so sit down and listen. This afternoon, Sebastian, while you were sitting with all the other hacks scribbling down the Chancellor's words of wisdom to the Treasury Committee in your little brown notebook – two doubles please, Reg – I have rolled up my sleeves and done some real work. You have been listening to the great ones of the land, I have been swopping tittle-tattle with chauffeurs and Chinese waiters. You have followed the herd, I have hunted alone. You –'

'I was only going to say –'

'Let me finish, Sebastian. You come here with your quaint ideas about parliamentary democracy and you think that, because this is the House of Commons, you're at the centre of events. You're not, you're nowhere near it. The things that really matter in politics don't happen here. They happen behind locked doors in the Department of Trade and Industry. They happen in smoky pubs in Liverpool. They happen in planes from Glasgow to Belfast. They happen in fields in Gloucestershire. In this case, they happen in the back rooms of Chinese restaurants in Soho. And you and I have to use our noses to find them. Not our brains, our noses. I don't know what the Chancellor said to get your knickers in such a twist but, whatever he did say, he said it to a million other people and it will be in all the other papers tomorrow. My story's a world exclusive. It's a sizzler. Strong men will gasp over their cornflakes. It involves nurses, Health Secretaries and shark's fins in some of the shadiest dealings ever seen in this country in peacetime. And when I tell you that for a modest outlay of £40 on salaries and £73.80 on refreshment –'

I paused. Sebastian's mouth had dropped open and he was making little gulping movements. It looked as though, if he didn't say his piece soon, he was going to asphyxiate.

'Come on,' I said wearily. 'Get it off your chest. What's happened?'

'The Chancellor's resigned,' he spluttered.

'What?'

'In protest at Feather having secret talks with the nurses. He announced it at the Treasury Committee.'

Time passes. One gets older. One gets wiser. Events which in one's youth seemed catastrophic, harbingers of a malignant Fate, no longer sear the soul. The dead weight of experience bears down on the fluttering wings of hope. Whisky numbs the senses. Bones creak as one walks upstairs. One farts a lot.

I must confess that this little fiasco with Sebastian was one of the low watermarks of my career in the House. Big stories had slipped through my fingers before. It happens. One shrugs and returns to the bar. But I'd never had such a powerful sense of the world turned sour, of losing out because other people had stopped playing the game. If Chancellors of the Exchequer were going to announce their resignation without so much as a nod and a wink beforehand, what price investigative journalism? Ex-Ministers are no use to man or beast. It's when they are still swanking around in their Ministers' Rovers with skeletons clanking in their cupboards that they have a function in life.

I ran into Spade a couple of weeks later and put this to him forcefully. He was just off to a job centre in the City to look for work and was in a bit of a hurry.

'Why did you go, Gordon?' I asked. 'You were a bloody awful Chancellor, but you weren't the first and you won't be the last. Why didn't you tough it out?'

'I couldn't, Beef. It was the principle of the thing.'

'Principle?' He had lost me.

'How could I possibly stay in the Treasury while that bastard Feather was in cahoots with the Prime Minister behind my back? He offered those nurses an extra one and a half per cent without even consulting me.'

I clicked. I was dealing with a moralist.

'That's £700 million, Beef. Of my money.'

They get like this, Chancellors. Give them the pursestrings and they think the money's theirs. When you get a mean Chancellor like Spade, he carries this burning image in his head of £180 billion earning interest for him in his savings account at the Nat West. It's a psychosexual problem.

'But, Gordon,' I protested. 'Why did you have to do it like that? Reading out a statement to the Treasury Committee? I've never heard of such a thing: it breaks every rule in the book. If you treat the press like monkeys, they'll never forgive you.'

'What's your problem, Beef? There must have been a hundred reporters in the room.'

'I dare say, Gordon. But not,' I said stiffly, 'the ones that counted.'

I dismissed him with a snarl. A Spade is a Spade is a Spade: you can't reason with them. The one bright spot in all this was that the new Chancellor was a racing man, so Budgets on Gold Cup day were out. Oh yes, there was one other thing. I'd almost forgotten . . .

A few days after all the excitement – I'd taken to my bed in shock – I hauled myself back up the stairs to the Press Bar. Who should be standing in the middle of the room with a new hair-cut and a grin the size of the M25 but Sebastian?

'What are you having, Beef? Drinks are on me.'

'It's not your birthday, is it?' I asked suspiciously. There was an undefined menace in the air. The situation had overtones of the time Ginger Hobbs arranged a gorillagram for his secretary and things got out of hand.

'No. I'm leaving.'

My heart missed a beat. 'Jumping ship, eh? Where are you going?'

'I've been head-hunted. I'm starting on a new paper after Easter.'

'*Gardener's Weekly*?'

'*Financial Times*.'

'That pink one with the numbers in? I've never tried it. Is it any good?'

'It should suit my style of work better.'

'That's true. You never had the finesse to be a tabloid man. And what,' I asked, suddenly noticing, 'is that you're drinking?'

'Just a pineapple juice.'

'*Pineapple*?'

'Yes.' He flushed and I was still reeling when he delivered the punch-line. 'I never told you this, Beef, but I got headaches drinking all that lager.'

5

MP IN LOCKJAW SENSATION

'This,' announced Ginger Hobbs, sidling up to me in the Press Bar and, with a flick of his wrist, sending my whisky flying across the room, 'is Heidi.'

I ordered another tumblerful and gave her the once-over. A bit over-perfumed, was my first impression, but you know how it is in press bars on a Thursday night: the smells swap around a bit and it's easy to mistake the Rémy Martin for the Chanel No 5.

'Hullo, Heidi. My name's John Wellington. You can call me Beef.'

'Hullo, Beef.'

'What can I get you?'

'G and t, please.'

'The usual, Ginger?'

'Thanks, Beef.'

I chucked a fiver at the barman and inspected Heidi in the mirror behind the Glenfiddich. She was fresh-faced, quite tall, and had one of those mops of hair which look as if they've been hacked off a sheep and left the sheep without much to see it through the winter. Light-middleweight in build, with arms like a butcher. Smiled a lot. From Ginger's anxious air, plus the fact that Heidi had been squashed into a suit whereas her demeanour was that of a woman used to slopping around in jeans and a T-shirt, I had the impression my opinion was being sought.

Ginger, I should explain, is one of those weak-minded men who can't go to *Mary Poppins* with a woman without first conducting a straw poll among his friends. His indecisiveness before taking the plunge is matched by his speed in scrambling out of the water once he's taken it. I don't know if his Hampshire constituents have ever mistaken him for Elizabeth Taylor or Zsa Zsa Gabor – it's unlikely, as he's a bespectacled dwarf, with a bald patch the size of Southampton – but his mating habits are oddly similar. Seven wives in fifteen years is fast work, even for a Member with a 20,000 majority who doesn't have to worry what the voters make of it all. But the sad thing is that, however often Ginger dips, so to speak, into the honey-pot, he comes out with a pawful of something which disagrees with him and either moves on to the next pot or explores alternative condiments like Marmite. Bad luck or bad management? I leave you to judge.

You're probably wondering why someone with a history of nipping into registry offices with also-rans should turn to me as his guide to form. Not Beef's trump suit, I hear you mutter, the man doesn't know one end of a female from another. It's like this. When Ginger's other friends were lining up like an honour-guard to stop him marrying that nice air-hostess Daphne (his third? no, fourth), I said, give it a whirl, Ginger, you never know; and when the said friends were frog-marching him to the altar with Sally Gray the novelist, I said, Ginger, you're off your trolley. To abbreviate the narrative, Daphne lasted five and a half years and Sally from September 11th to 19th inclusive and Ginger, remembering my well-chosen words, has since invested me with the clairvoyance of an Old Testament prophet. He asked me to be best man sixth time round and, if he hadn't cocked up the dates and got spliced during the second circuit of the Mackeson Gold Cup, I would have humoured the poor fool. We have an understanding, you might say.

As Ginger was currently unlet property – Robyn, his seventh, had left him for a Romanian trapeze-artist – and

was giving Heidi the adoring gaze of a well-fed cocker span-
iel on a charm offensive, you didn't need a master's degree
in biology to see which way the wind was blowing. Always
happy to do the decent thing by a friend, I handed the
happy couple their drinks and submitted Heidi to some
stern questioning.

'You like a drink in the evening, do you?'

'Yeah.'

'Good-time girl?'

'Yeah.'

'Easy-going, tolerant type?'

'Yeah.'

'No history of anorexia in the family?'

'Anna who?'

'He means undereating,' said Ginger quickly. 'You've
got a good appetite, haven't you, darling? You like a big
supper?'

'Oh. Yeah.'

You know, the more I talked to Heidi, the more I liked
her. Simple, straightforward, honest, nothing sharp or off-
centre in her answers. Met my questions head on and came
up trumps every time. An absolute munchkin. People who
go in for this marriage guidance caper in a professional
capacity will tell you that, if a couple are going to bed-and-
breakfast together till the Last Trump sounds, it's important that they shouldn't just do the business in the bedroom,
but be able to hold long meaningful conversations over the
nightly Ovaltine. Bollocks, as my granny used to say.
Ginger's first three spouses could talk the hind legs off a
donkey, but that was the trouble. Ginger, like many don-
keys, functions better with his hind legs on and, in Heidi's
lilting yeahs, I detected just what the doctor ordered – a
woman who would make no demands. A lovely man,
Ginger. Warm, open, generous to a fault. But demands he
can't handle.

When he had shown Heidi off the premises and come
back to hear the jury's verdict, I gave the immediate
thumbs-up.

'Order the champagne and carnations, Ginger. This one will see out the century.'

'You think so, Beef?'

'I do think so. A real find. Helen of Troy and Lot's wife rolled into one. I don't know how you do it.'

'I was in this pub in Petersfield –'

'Spare me the sordid details, old cock. I haven't had supper yet. When's the wedding? Tomorrow? Saturday?'

'Not just yet. You see, Beef, and this is what I have to talk to you about, there's a slight hitch.'

'Parents disapprove?'

'No, it's not that. Heidi's interested in politics.'

'She'll get over it.'

'I hope so, Beef. The trouble is, what she *really* wants – it's ridiculous, but she keeps wanting it, that's what's so bloody – is to hear me speak in the House.'

I gripped the side of the bar and practically choked on my drink.

'You don't mean –'

'Yes.'

'You're not telling me –'

'Yes.'

'If you want to marry that woman, you've got to get up on your hind legs in the menagerie and make a speech?'

'More or less.'

'Oh God. Oh Christ. Oh Ginger.'

'Exactly.'

I swayed on my stool and for a few seconds the whole world went dark.

You're probably scratching your head pretty vigorously by now. Why should an elected Member of Parliament, a class of person not known for reticence, undergo these paroxysms of terror at the prospect of making a speech? It's what they're paid for, isn't it?

Yes and no. It's true that the typical backbencher is no wallflower: give him five minutes' air-time and he will grab it like a man beating a woman to a seat on the 6.07 from

Waterloo. But you get exceptions which prove the rule. And there are quite a few MPs who, while involving themselves heavily behind the scenes, have so little flair for oratory that they stay out of the limelight.

In Ginger's case, which is admittedly extreme, he made a three-minute maiden speech in 1975 and hasn't uttered since. Not even at Questions or in committee. He was in the Whips Office for thirteen years – Whips are debarred from speaking in the House and furniture would be broken if they tried – but that was a cover for his silence, not the real explanation. To understand Ginger's Trappist tendencies, you need to go back to that maiden speech.

I was in the bar, funnily enough, when his name came up on the annunciator screen. Maiden speeches aren't everyone's cup of tea – they're a bit like school nativity plays, the shorter the better – but my nose for banana-skins made me wander into the gallery. I'd taken a liking to young Ginger Hobbs, or plain Abercrombie Hobbs as he was then: he had the look of one of those friendly, complaisant types who sit around in bars and laugh at other people's jokes and generally oil the great wheels of life. He was also a monumentally clumsy man. I'd seen him knock over three glasses of wine in Annie's in half an hour without breaking sweat; so it seemed even money, when he rose to make his maiden speech, that he would somehow contrive to trip over his feet and make a prize turkey of himself.

I was not disappointed.

The debate was on defence and it was a thin House: a couple of dozen Members sleeping, about the same number awake. Ginger was speaking from his usual place, three rows back below the gangway, and had struck what you might call a Churchillian posture, leading with his chin and chest. A bit risky striking Churchillian postures when you stand at four feel eleven in your shoes and don't have a chin or chest to speak of: the mind turns, not to the late Sir Winston, but to mating frogs. But it's a mistake a lot of them make.

He was obviously nervous as a kitten. His hands were shaking and an early intimation of trouble came when he addressed Mr Speaker as Mr Squeaker. The first duty of every Government, he went on quickly, was to defend its citizens – which would have been stirring stuff if he hadn't got his tongue in a twist and said 'offend' instead. And so it went on. Anyone else would have got the bird, but it's an inviolable rule in the House that maiden speeches are listened to without heckling or interruption; and, although amused smiles could be seen on the faces of the Opposition, nobody actually threw anything. Even when he dropped his speaking notes, which proceeded to float halfway across the House like a paper aeroplane, there were only the faintest murmurings and those of sympathy. If it hadn't been for the final disaster, he would have made it to the end with his dignity intact.

But it was not to be. Like many Members, Ginger's first action on rising to speak had been to do up the middle button of his jacket. I believe this is what psychiatrists call a defence mechanism. When people are nervous of a social situation, they do all sorts of things with their bodies – fiddling with their ties, adjusting their cuff-links, folding their arms – to erect barriers between themselves and the approaching terror. (This is all quite kosher: I saw a programme about it on BBC2.) In Ginger's case, he would have been better advised to fiddle with his tie. Middle buttons are notorious at the best of times and, when striking a Churchillian posture, are definitely untrustworthy. To cut a long story short, he thrust out his chest once too often and, with a trajectory which many rehearsals couldn't have improved on, the button flew across the Chamber and struck the Serjeant at Arms on the side of the head.

The Serjeant at Arms, in case you're wondering, is the elderly citizen in fancy dress who sits by the entrance to the Chamber, sword at the ready, like a sentry in grand opera. Had he been awake, he could probably have taken a high-velocity button in his stride. As he was sunk in a profound slumber, he overestimated the gravity of the situation and, in a blood-curdling voice which I can still hear, shouted 'Fire!'

At which point the hitherto well-behaved Opposition

Members decided enough was enough and gave Ginger the right royal runaround . . .

'You know what I remember?' he said bitterly, the wounds still fresh sixteen years on. 'The sheer *venom* with which they laughed. It could have happened to any one of them, but they didn't have the humanity to see that. They just pointed their fingers and howled.'

'It was rather funny, Ginger.'

'And the press,' he went on, turning his bitterness on me. 'Totally unsympathetic. Totally. I'll never forget that piece you wrote the next day. You said I had sacrificed a lucrative career in a travelling circus.'

'Forgive and forget, Ginger.'

'You said that, if the England junior tiddly-winks team was looking for someone to make up the numbers, it need look no further than this master of the well-aimed button.'

'Just doing my job, Ginger.'

'You said that, not only did I need a new tailor and speech-writer, but I would have to invest in a pair of stilts or I would be mistaken for a performing mouse.'

'Flea, I think, Ginger. Performing flea.'

'Flea or mouse, what do you have to say for yourself, you bastard?'

'I think,' I said, ordering him another drink and waiting for him to simmer down, 'we should let bygones be bygones. There's this little matter of Heidi. Is she serious about wanting you to make a speech?'

'Perfectly. She goes on and on about it. She thinks it would turn her on, bring out the statesman in me.'

'Statesman? Turn her on? What, you in that monkey-house?'

'I know, it's revolting.'

'And she seemed so normal.'

'She is normal. She's lovely, Beef, she's perfect, you saw what a poppet she is. She's just got this one little kink. Oh, Beef, Beef, what am I going to do?'

I put a consoling hand on his shoulder. You couldn't help

feeling sorry for the poor stick-insect. As an advertisement for celibacy, it took a lot of beating. If I'd known when I bought this Jezebel her gin and tonic that, beneath the friendly smile and the mop of hair and the economy of language, there lurked a screaming pervert who got her rocks off at the thought of Ginger Hobbs delivering the Gettysburg Address, I would have separated them with a crowbar. But you know how it is with some men. Once they have got a bit of skirt between their teeth, they won't be parted with it at any money.

'You'll just have to go ahead with it,' I said, trying to introduce a note of sternness into the conversation.

He boggled. 'How can I possibly go ahead with it? I haven't made a speech in sixteen years. I'd make a complete fool of myself.'

'You must make speeches in your constituency? Party fundraisers? Church fêtes? School prize-givings?'

'Never. Never. I just get up, say I'm sure they don't want to hear their Member of Parliament make a speech ha ha and sit down again.'

'That gets a good hand, does it?'

'Every time. Every bloody time. You wouldn't believe how popular a politician with lockjaw is. My majority's gone up at every election.' He took a gulp of whisky, looked heavenwards for inspiration, then banged his head against the wall in the hope it was all a dream. It wasn't. He shuddered. 'It's no good, Beef, I can't do it.'

'You can, Ginger.'

'I can't, Beef.'

'You can, Ginger.'

'I can't, Beef.'

'You can, Ginger.'

And, as this sort of conversation makes me throb around the temples, I drew up a plan of campaign on the back of an envelope, stage one of which took Ginger and me to the village of Little Diddlington-on-Hump, on the borders of his constituency, on the Friday following.

*

(5) the Spanish ambassador joke;

(6) the story of the Home Secretary, the ham sandwich and the delegation from South Korea.

I'd seen Ginger set Annie's alight with all these items and, whether he had them rolling in the aisles now, I anticipated he would have no difficulty remembering his lines. And, on that point, I was right. The Speaker Gulley story was flawlessly delivered and, if some of the women were stony-faced, reflecting that the annual sub to the Historical Society was £5 and for that money they deserved something more elevated, the woman in the second row with the sea-gull impressions excelled herself and was briefly in danger of falling off her chair. Ginger drank it all in like a man inhaling oxygen and moved on to the next item. This too was going well, you could say swimmingly – until, just as he was nearing the punch-line, the doors at the back of the hall opened and, like a rushing wind, a hundred and fifty schoolgirls trouped in.

I couldn't swear to the fifty because I lost count after a hundred, but there were three coaches on the green opposite and you can stuff an awful lot of schoolgirls into a coach if you're in the stuffing business. It wasn't really the numbers which shocked, so much as the look on the little devils' faces: sly, malevolent, unforgiving. Here, you felt, and you felt it keenly, are a hundred and fifty pubescent females who've been cooped up in a coach for an hour and a half and are about to let off steam like the Stephenson Rocket. Blood will be spilt, you felt. Strong men will weep. The French Revolution will seem like a picnic. The human being in me was feeling mighty sorry for Ginger. The journalist couldn't sharpen his pencil fast enough.

Miss Raines clapped her hands. 'I'd better stop you there, Mr Hobbs, while the girls take their places. Hurry up, girls.' There was a scramble for seats and, within seconds, the audience was settled. 'Carry right on, Mr Hobbs,' she said, with a brisk confidence in her voice which seemed to hit Ginger in the solar plexus like a lorry-load of sledge-hammers.

I would be rewriting the history of rural Hampshire if I said he was unperturbed by these developments. As I don't want to appear before the Press Council, I'll give you the facts straight. He was horribly perturbed. I don't know if you've visited the aquarium at London Zoo and found your-self face to face with one of those large, bulging-eyed fish which look as if they're trying to blow smoke rings? Ginger's jaw movements were strikingly similar. He looked to me for help, then he looked to Miss Raines, then his eyes lit on a door marked FIRE EXIT and a longing for the open spaces seemed to overwhelm him: his chest heaved and he started pawing the ground like a wild stallion about to charge across the prairie. He was on the point of exiting when, in an effort to be helpful, Miss Raines intervened.

'Mr Hobbs was just telling us an amusing story about the House of Commons, girls. There was apparently an MP before the war called Charlie Varley – did I get that name right, Mr Hobbs?'

'Yes, yes. Oh very. Oh quite.'

'Who was given a bright orange tie for Christmas by – was it his wife or his sister, Mr Hobbs?'

'Sister. No, wife. Doesn't matter, doesn't matter.'

'Well, anyway, that was where we'd got to, girls, and as I don't know the rest of the story, I'd better let Mr Hobbs carry on. Mr Hobbs.'

Here the girls gave Ginger what would have been a very decent round of applause, had it not been for the loud whist-ling in the upper register which sounded pretty much like wolves at one end of the Russian steppes trying to catch the attention of their loved ones at the other. I'd had the opportunity to study the little monsters while Ginger was doing his fish impressions and two ominous points had struck me:

(1) they were accompanied by only one adult, a dowdy woman in glasses who had the presence and natural authority of a mouse with a speech defect; and

(2) from the fumes issuing from the contingent breathing down my neck, the whole lot were high on Strongbow cider. (I have a nose for drink and can identify a hundred and forty-four brands by smell alone.)

Ginger cleared his throat. 'Charlie Varley MP –' he began, whereupon there were about seventy-five interventions from a sedentary position of which I jotted down the following selection.

'You're the charlie.'

'Speak up, baldy.'

'We've heard it, we've heard it.'

'God, he's a dwarf.'

'Are you our Member?'

'Not very big for a member.'

'Hurry up, I have to pee.'

'What a wally/creep/cretin/prick/dickhead.'

'If I could be allowed to *continue*,' Ginger shouted at the top of his voice. I'd never seen him so angry: it was awe-inspiring. He was so much the dominant male that he stopped the hecklers in their tracks and, for about a second and a half, there was complete silence. Attaboy, Ginger, I thought, give 'em the works. And the works is what he would have given them, for he was mad as a fighting cock, if he hadn't at that moment received one of those knees in the groin from Fate which made the ancient Greeks push away their moussaka untasted and swop bitter one-liners about hubris and nemesis. Suiting the action to the word in textbook fashion, he thumped the table with a vigour which, had the table been located where he thought, would have cowed the whole mob into submission for the rest of the evening, cider or no cider.

The table was not so located. It was some eighteen inches distant, with the result that his descending fist had nothing on which to descend; and so violent was his follow-through that he lost his footing and had to cling on to the lectern for support. This, too, was not positioned quite where he supposed . . .

The audience reaction was lively and spontaneous. When there's mayhem in the Commons and the boys in Hansard are too pissed to take down what everyone's said, they resort to the catch-phrase '[*Interruptions*]'. I will simply report that there were interruptions and that Abercrombie Hobbs Esq, MP lost consciousness a few minutes later.

He came to the following morning in Fleet hospital, with me by his bedside working my way through a bunch of grapes donated, in deepest sympathy, by the Little Diddlington Historical Society. He groaned, stared around, got his bearings, then gripped my hand like a drowning man.

'Have they gone?' he whispered. 'Please tell me they've gone.'

'They've gone.'

'They're not lurking somewhere? Lying in wait?'

'You're perfectly safe, Ginger. They're back behind bars.'

'You're sure, Beef? You're quite sure? Who's that over there?'

'The senior anaesthetist. Ginger, please. Stop talking and breathe normally. You're going to be all right.'

He subsided into his pillow and stared up at the ceiling. His face had a grey, desolate quality, as if he'd been to Hell and back and didn't care what happened in the second half

'Does Heidi know?' he murmured.

'Yes and no. She knows you're in hospital and she's on her way. I don't know if she's young enough to believe what she reads in newspapers, but her perception of events is likely to be coloured by this.'

I took a newspaper cutting out of my pocket and showed it to him.

MP COLLAPSES
Hampshire MP Abercrombie Hobbs collapsed yesterday after a speaking engagement in his constituency. He was

taken to Fleet hospital and held overnight for observation.

Earlier, in a rare and wide-ranging speech, Mr Hobbs had dazzled a packed meeting in Little Diddlington with his charm, erudition and wit. He expects to resume his parliamentary duties next week.

'I thought,' I said quickly, seeing the blood surge to his cheeks, 'that it would be a good idea to gloss over the facts. Heidi still wants you to make that speech in the House and, if she knew you'd slipped up in training, she might start doubting your penchant for oratory.'

He sat angrily up in bed. 'I'm not making any bloody speech in the House. If you think, after that fiasco last night –'

'Just a temporary setback, Ginger.'

'I'd like to know what you call a permanent setback, you fat slob. Cancer of the head? The electric chair? It's no good, Beef. I'll tell Heidi exactly what happened and rely on her sympathy.'

'Did you say sympathy?'

'She's a loving, generous woman. She's bound to sympathise.'

This was obvious delirium. I summoned the nurse to administer a sedative and, when Ginger had had a needleful in the arse, gave it to him straight.

'Ginger, listen. There are men playing the mouth organ on street corners who've relied on women's sympathy. There are men sleeping in cardboard boxes on the Embankment who've made the same mistake. If you think Heidi's going to turn up at the registry office in her glad rags when you've told her about last night, you're a sick man. She'll rally round and she'll make you mugs of cocoa, but love will droop and passion wither on the vine. Honestly, Ginger. Women don't want men they can feel sorry for. They want men standing outside the cave with a club in their hand and a dead bison slung over their shoulder.'

'Daphne felt sorry for me.'

'Daphne *understood* you, Ginger. Not the same. Now about this speech.'

'Bugger the speech.'

'I've been looking at next week's business in the Commons and Friday looks an absolute peach. "A debate on EEC forestry proposals on a motion for the adjournment of the House." If that doesn't clear the lobbies and jam the exits, nothing will. The place will be like a morgue.'

'What do I know about forestry?'

'Bluff. Talk about Scotch pines and Sitka spruces and tell them the one about the squirrel and the chestnut. I'll make sure Heidi's in the gallery.'

'The squirrel and the chestnut?'

'It's perfectly clean, I got it from my granny. You'll have an audience of two men and a dog and not a schoolgirl in sight. After yesterday it will be a breeze. What about it, Ginger?'

He looked at me and, for a second, he was tempted. Then visions of homicidal schoolgirls swam before his eyes and he writhed on the pillow.

'It's no good, Beef. I'm finished, I've made my last speech. You can't make me go through that hell again.'

'One last effort, Ginger.'

'No, Beef.'

'Think of Heidi.'

'No, Beef.'

'Your luck will turn. It always does.'

'Never. Never. Never.'

And, having reached this impasse, we made no further progress until we lunched together on chicken curry and rhubarb crumble on the following Friday. The crumble was immaterial. The curry was critical.

One of the few nice things about being a lobby correspondent is the perks. The pay's lousy, the hours are ghastly, but the fringe benefits are something else. Pluck a backbencher from obscurity and quote one of his pronouncements in a national organ and he'll go to considerable lengths to show his appreciation. A bottle of Scotch at Christmas is the usual tariff, but some Members are more expansive and, as I sat down to lunch with Ginger, I still had on my person a packet of dope given to me the night before by one of the *nouvelle vague* of Glasgow Members. 'Lebanese black,' he had whispered conspiratorially. 'Top quality.'

I'm not normally a drugs man. Tobacco, yes. Alcohol, yes please. But marihuana I don't rate and nor do my bowels: give them a litre of plonk and an eighteen-ounce steak any day. This wad of hash in my pocket was frankly an embarrassment and I had made a mental note to dispose of it before some eager constable took it into his head to search me. As Ginger spotted a constituent and nipped off to say hullo, leaving his curry unguarded, an unholy thought erupted in my head.

Well, wouldn't it have erupted in your head? Never mind the ethics, consider the facts:

(1) in my pocket, a prohibited substance meriting a hefty fine or a spell in jug;
(2) sitting opposite me, a social misfit incapable of making a simple speech without some powerful stimulus to his nervous system;
(3) on the table in front of him, a plate of curry so virulent you could have poured on a bottle of methylated spirits without altering the taste.

What was I to do? It was the work of a moment to spike the curry and, when Ginger returned and tucked in, he didn't notice a thing.

The drug's effect was slow but sure. It was twelve twenty when he started on the curry and by quarter to one he was visibly frisky. I tested him with a not very funny joke and he giggled like a schoolboy. By one fifteen you could see the whites of his eyes and by one thirty he was as high as a pre-war pheasant. When I mentioned that the forestry debate was still in progress, the effect was electric.

'I think I ought to intervene,' he said, springing to his feet.

'Ginger, you're not going to make a speech?'

'Try stopping me. The Forestry Minister's a cretin and it's about time someone told him. I've got a bit of the New Forest in my constituency, so I know what I'm talking about. Did I ever tell you the one about the squirrel and the chestnut? I forget the punch-line, but it goes well without it. So long, Beef.'

And, gliding off like a ship in sail, he headed straight for the Chamber. I rang Heidi to tell her to get a ringside seat and was in the gallery before you could say 'Lebanese pot makes a man pottier.'

The debate, as anticipated, was thinly attended. There were fewer than a dozen Members in the Chamber and, after the speaker who had the floor, a Scot called McCallendar, it would be time for the closing speeches from the front benches. Ginger was sitting on his own in the front row below the gangway. Nobody had paid him much attention but, if you had the inside gen and studied him, he had lost contact with the real world. His head was rotating clock-wise, his eyes anti-clockwise and his nose, though this may have been a trick of the light, seemed to be wrinkling and unwrinkling in six-eight time. There, you thought, with a mixture of awe and apprehension, sits a man who doesn't give a brass farthing what the world thinks of him.

McCallendar concluded his remarks and the Opposition spokesman on forestry rose to his feet. So, with a nipping and an eager air, did Ginger. The Speaker hesitated.

'Is the Honourable gentleman leaving the Chamber?'

Ginger bowed gracefully. 'Far from it, Mr Speaker. As a matter of fact, I was hoping to catch your eye.'

The Speaker shot him a suspicious look. 'Is the Honourable gentleman saying he wants to make a speech?'

'In a very small nutshell – that is to say, yes, Mr Speaker. With the leave of the House?'

'Very well. Mr Abercrombie Hobbs.'

The Opposition spokesman resumed his seat with a frown. He threw enquiring glances at his colleagues, who shook their heads in bewilderment. The Minister whispered something to the Whip. The Serjeant at Arms adjusted his glasses. A speech from Ginger, you must remember, had the novelty value of an intervention from the Member for Mars Central: as his name went up on the annunciator screen, I could imagine people in other parts of the building staring at it in disbelief and deciding they must have had one too many at lunchtime.

Ginger raised a finger dramatically in the air, like a cricket umpire, and let rip.

'The Sitka spruce, which is not to be confused with the Scotch pine, is one of those hardy conifers which, by proliferating in such numbers in Scotland, has both benefited the forestry industry and, at the same time and through no fault of its own, created alarm and despondency among those of our friends, citizens and constituents who love the countryside as God made it and wish to see its natural beauty conserved for their children, not disfigured by row upon row of trees planted out with the guidance issued by the Forestry Commission.'

I've set out this sentence as it appeared the next day in Hansard, without capturing the sing-song quality in the delivery which made such a vivid impression. Close your eyes, ignore the content, and you could have been listening to the winning entry in the National Eisteddfod of Wales. It soothed the ear with the effect of harmony. It was rather beautiful.

He continued in the same vein, wagging his finger, wobbling his vowels, spinning his crazy theories, making learned references to cellulose and acid rain and native pine woods and generally giving an A1 impersonation of a man who'd drunk a vat of Glenfiddich and been challenged to recite everything he knew about trees in five minutes without irrelevance or repetition. The other Members were spellbound: they had never heard anything like it. Heidi sat goggling in the gallery. The Hansard reporter was so mesmerised he stopped writing. An absurd feeling of pride gripped me – it was one of my masterpieces.

He was just broaching the subject of squirrels and chestnuts when the heavy mob arrived in the shape of six tough-looking gorillas from the Government Whips Office. They stood pointing and giggling by the entrance to the Chamber, then moved forward to form a doughnut – the group of Members who sit immediately behind the Member speaking for the benefit of television. The next time Ginger paused for breath, one of them got smoothly to his feet.

'Will my Honourable friend give way?'

Ginger pirouetted elegantly, nodded and resumed his seat.

'I'm grateful to my Honourable friend. Can he explain something about squirrels which has always puzzled me? How are grey squirrels distinguished from red squirrels in the EEC proposals the House is debating?'

Ginger rose shakily to reply. He was delivering what was basically an aria and the intervention of a second voice had disoriented him.

'I'm afraid I don't quite follow my Honourable friend's question,' he mumbled. 'I should need notice of it.'

Three more members of the doughnut leapt to their feet, grinning wickedly.

'Could my Honourable friend say something about 1992?'

'Could my Honourable friend share his thoughts on red deer with the House?'

'Could my Honourable friend extend his remarks about acid rain to what is happening in the Brazilian rain-forests?'

It was like a balloon bursting. Ginger opened his mouth to say something, but nothing came out, not a sausage. He stood there in total silence, a small, frightened, inconsequential figure with not a spark of fire left in his belly.

'I think you're all horrible,' he whispered at last, resuming his seat. When one of the hecklers said something, he spun round and, in a fit of rage, threw one of the best punches I've ever seen. It wouldn't have disgraced the Red Lion in Hackney at chucking-out time on a Saturday night. But Westminster isn't Hackney, more's the pity, and as the Speaker's duty when punches are thrown is set out in black and white in the Standing Orders, he had to leave the Chamber in short order.

It was with heavy heart that I intercepted him five minutes later in the Central Lobby. I'd done my best for the poor simpleton and all for nothing. As I put an arm round his shoulder and said it had been good while it lasted but, on mature consideration, I would advise him to resume his career in Trappism, I don't mind admitting I felt a bit of a heel.

At this point Heidi appeared at the other end of the lobby.

I feared the worst, but she flung her arms round Ginger and, in the warm, unmistakable tones of hero-worship, whispered: 'Ginge, you were terrific, just terrific. The way you hit that man! Oh, Ginger.'

And with the reflection that it takes all sorts to make a world but that, for sheer perfidy, you can't beat women who ask for oratory when what they really want is a good punch-up, I trickled diplomatically away.

6

PORKY SECRET OF MAD DOC'S HUBBY

The return of Dr Hilda Ann Bosworth for the county constituency of Merryvale, a good-looking piece of real estate
between Manchester and Edinburgh, to the left of the map
as you look at it, spelled hassle with a big H.

I hadn't kept tabs on the by-election, which coincided
with the Lord's Test and the AGM of my local malt whisky
society, but I was truffling through one of the Sunday
middle-brows over a light lunch of steak and kidney pudding and apple charlotte when a diary entry shot up off
the page and practically brained me. 'Merryvale's new MP
Hilda Bosworth, author of the best-selling diet book *Cholesterol Kills* . . .' I read it twice, then had to lurch to the fridge
for another beer. This, I remember thinking as the beer slid
down my throat, marks the end of civilisation as we know
it.

It may not come across loud and clear from these little
jottings, but I have a great affection for Members of Parliament. When I pass them in a corridor, I want them to greet
me with a cheery smile which I can return with an even
cheerier. A cynic, if there was such a thing in politics, would
say I was just using them for my purposes as they were
using me for theirs; that it was a relationship of convenience.
I don't share that view. We may be earning our crust in
the Palace of Westminster doing different things, but we're
human beings and the Fleet Street half of the pantomime

horse are civilised human beings. A cordial understanding is the order of the day. I believe there's a French expression to the same effect.

But would such a rapport be possible with a visitor from the further shores of fitness freakery? I had my doubts. And when Dr B took her seat in the House the next day, my worst fears were confirmed.

These occasions are usually among the friskier parliamentary rituals and provide light relief between Questions and the main business of the day. The newly elected Member waits with two supporters at the Bar of the House – not what you and I would call a bar, just a white line on the carpet, much as you would see in the middle of the A40 – until the Speaker calls out: 'Members desirous of taking their seats will be pleased to come to the Table.' The new Member then bows once to the Chair, walks forward five paces, bows again, walks another five paces and bows a third time. If this is achieved without mishap – and I know one Member, now in the Cabinet, who made such a botch of it he took one step too many, bowed in the wrong direction and toppled into the lap of the Leader of the Opposition – the Member takes the Oath (an obscure sixteenth-century expletive whispered to him by the Clerk), shakes hands with the Speaker and, if he's got any sense, heads straight down to the bar. The real bar. All this to a soundtrack of cheers and booing – cheers from the party which has won the seat, boos from the other lot. If the new Member's a woman, of course, the men all give her the once over and ditto if it's a man but vice versa, if you see what I mean. All good clean fun. You could take your maiden aunt to it.

Hilda Bosworth's introduction lacked the usual hilarity, however, and I'll tell you why. She was a very *serious* woman. Put her next to a Mother Superior in one of the stricter orders and she'd make the latter look like a go-go girl who had overdone the Bacardi on a night out. Tall, neatly dressed, her hair severely short, she stood at the Bar of the House with such an air of solemnity that the hearty welcome the House was preparing froze on everyone's lips. She walked forward to take the Oath with a weird, almost military, precision – and you could hear a pin drop. I've known Bully Potter of Somerset Central throw his order paper at new Members when the Speaker wasn't looking, but even he was silenced. I felt pretty queasy myself.

As luck would have it, I ran into the woman half an hour later. I was making my way from the Press Bar, where the beer is better, to Annie's, where they have a nice line in peanuts, when I spotted her coming out of the Whips Office – a padded cell off the Members Lobby, next to the room where they keep the thumbscrews. And she spotted me. I'm fairly easy to spot, of course, taking up more than my share of the horizon, but I like to think that, having been around the place more than twenty years, I fade inoffensively into the background. Not a bit of it. Her jaw sagged, she let out an anguished 'Good God!' and, heels clicking nineteen to the dozen like the guards' jackboots at Colditz Castle, marched towards me across the lobby. Calculating our respective speeds at three miles per hour and 0 to 60 in twelve seconds, I stood my ground.

'How do you do?' I said, holding out a sweaty hand which she ignored. 'My name's John Wellington. Better known as Beef.'

'Well, I hope you're doing something about it,' she said darkly.

I couldn't make that one out, so I scratched my ear. 'We'll be seeing a bit of each other around the place,' I went on gaily. 'I'm a lobby correspondent. Sort of failed journalist. May I call you Hilda?'

'What *are* you doing about it, Mr Wellington?' she repeated.

I scratched my ear again. It was no good, she'd lost me. 'Between ourselves, the paper I write for isn't all that big on politics, although its coverage of the female anatomy is encyclopaedic. But if you're prepared to take a lighter view of parliamentary life –'

'I mean, *this*.' And, like a farmer prodding livestock, she poked me hard in the stomach. Between the fifth and sixth buttons of my shirt. Painful spot.

'Now, look here –' I protested. There was a party of schoolchildren tramping past on their way to the Strangers Gallery. I just hoped she was going to keep it clean.

'Do you know what happens to people like you, Mr Wellington?' she asked, talking very rapidly between clenched teeth. 'I'll tell you. They eat more and more of the wrong sort of food and they drink more and more of the wrong sort of drink and the cholesterol builds up and up and up and the arteries get more and more blocked and the heart gets more and more at risk and they *die*, Mr Wellington. I've seen it happen hundreds of times. Stupid, fat, complacent, short-sighted, pig-headed *men* who eat total garbage and drink themselves silly every night of the year. I'm telling you: if you don't lay off the booze and the fatty foods and whatever else you've been abusing that disgusting body of yours with, you'll be gone before you're sixty. I mean it.'

Quite a bollocking. But it takes more than a left and right to the jaw to floor Beef Wellington and I duly delivered a counterpunch. One of my very best efforts.

'It's odd you should say that,' I said, politely removing her digit from my navel. 'Because I was seventy-seven last birthday.'

And, leaving her reeling backwards like one of those characters in a Kung Fu film who is shortly going to require a stretcher, I cut a magisterial swathe to the bar.

For two or three weeks, nothing happened. That is to say, I looked carefully round every corner for any sign of this harpy and, by a mixture of good luck and good management, avoided her.

On July 11th she made her maiden speech in the House and I sneaked into the Gallery to listen. It was one of those spine-chilling occasions which still has me waking with a scream at three o'clock in the morning. The debate was supposed to be about the National Health Service, but she turned it into a one-woman slanging match about the

British diet. Foodstuff after foodstuff she lambasted, all the old favourites like Yorkshire pudding and spotted dick, until the only things left on the menu were lentils, soya beans and, if memory serves, a special sort of lettuce you could get in Harrod's. Then she turned to the subject of drink. Strong men quaked in their seats. There was total silence. I could see poor old Tom Brazen of Nottingham – who doesn't so much have a bloodstream as a ginstream and whom I once saw eat seven bacon sandwiches in Annie's at a sitting – staring at her in fixed horror like a rabbit looking down the barrel of a gun. My heart bled for the man. If the voters of Merryvale had known, when they signed on the dotted line, that they were going to be spoken for by one of the biggest loonies to come out of medical school, they would have turned out by the coach-load to vote in the Flat-Earth candidate.

Then, on July 13th, came the second incident. I was taking lunch in the cafeteria off Westminster Hall and, for reasons that are neither here nor there, taking it against the background of a missed breakfast. There was ground to be made up, in other words, and when I tell you my chips were piled up on a second plate because there wasn't room on the first, you'll have some idea of the scale of the under-taking.

I had just taken the lid off the mayonnaise and tomato ketchup and was about to make free with them, when the doctor loomed over the horizon. She was carrying what at first appeared to be an empty tray, but on closer inspection housed a small salad, an apple and a thimbleful of coffee. She deposited this lot opposite me and, with the breezy directness which was becoming her signature-tune, barked, 'Are you planning to eat that?'

I enjoy conversation over lunch as a general rule and am always happy to punctuate the troughing with some light badinage. As the doctor's opening gambit fell outside this category by about the width of the Thames at high tide, I gravely opened my copy of the *Guardian*, propped it against the ketchup and started to read the racing section.

'You heard me,' she said, sending the *Guardian* flying into the chips. 'Are you planning to eat that rubbish?'

I opened my mouth to say something terse and Anglo-Saxon, but she came right at me like a terrier.

'And don't try that line about being seventy-seven. You're fifty-three because I looked it up. And you weigh –'

A rather tense interview followed, of which the particulars need not detain us.

'This,' I announced to the tea-time clientele in Annie's: Lennie, Tom, Bill, Arthur, the usual crowd, 'is war. I've been working in this second-rate music-hall for twenty years and I've never come across anything like it. She comes here with her two thousand majority and her medical qualifications and her snotty manner and she starts throwing her weight about like a night-club bouncer on the Costa del Sol. Such weight as she has,' I added darkly, for I was in bitter mood.

'Just ignore her, Beef,' said Lenny.

'Tell her to get knotted,' called Arthur from the other end of the bar.

'Can't you dish some dirt on her?' suggested Tom from the *Argus*.

'I would if I could, Tom,' I groaned. 'The trouble with women like the Bosworth is there's never any dirt to dish on them. They're squeaky clean, which is why they have the gall to lecture the rest of us. Do I pick on teetotallers? Do I victimise people who eat salads? Do I hound joggers off the street? This place has been a symbol of tolerance and reasonableness and give-and-take for seven hundred years. If out-to-lunch quacks like this she-devil are going to get elected, we might as well go and write for the sports page. I mean it.' And I would have sobbed into my whisky if it hadn't already had a generous covering of soda.

'There must be some dirt on her,' Tom persisted. 'There's dirt on everyone.' He's a gloomy bugger, with an even lower opinion of human nature than me.

'Well, I'd like to know about it,' I said. 'Before I strangle the woman. Another double please, George.'

Which explains, in a roundabout way, why I found myself, the following Saturday, in the Goat and Thistle in Merryvale, about five miles from the Mongolian border.

It's generally accepted in the circles in which I move that, if you want to get the low-down on someone, you instal yourself at their local hostelry, charge a vat and a half of whisky to expenses and wait for some well-lubricated tongue to loose its moorings. The alternative is to crawl around in your victim's shrubbery with a pair of heavy-duty binoculars. I didn't dawdle over the choice.

But tongues loosing themselves from their moorings there weren't. The Goat and Thistle is one of those remote rural establishments which, while providing the services advertised – the landlord pulled me a pint of the murkiest and said 'There you are, squire' in his best saloon-bar English – is a bit short of what the French call *Le razzmatazz*. The only other inmate when I arrived was an elderly freemason with a beard who was deep in an article about fly-fishing in the *Daily Telegraph*. (I'm guessing about the freemason bit, but I wouldn't give you more than six to four against.) When I asked him what he thought of his new Member, he got hold of the wrong end of the stick and, at the sort of length which makes strong men's jaws sag into their beer, talked me through his recent hip replacement operation. Not pretty.

Next in to bat was a visitor from the planet Mercury with a sheep in tow. I kid you not. He strode into the bar with one of the mangiest animals I've ever seen, explained to the landlord it was poorly and having to see a vet, then allowed it to pad about sniffing the customers' genitals while he grumbled to anyone who cared to listen about the Common Agricultural Policy and the fact that it hadn't rained for a fortnight. I downed my beer, kicked the sheep where I thought sheep kept their testicles and left. I have my standards.

There was a walk of about ten yards to where I had parked the car – I don't believe in turning these bucolic outings into point-to-points – but it was ten yards too far. I was stopping for a breather halfway when I became conscious of an enemy vessel closing fast from starboard. Herself, no less. Well, it was her constituency.

'You,' she said, in a glum voice.

'Me,' I admitted, giving her pound for pound glumnesswise.

'What –?' she asked.

'A holiday,' I replied quickly.

'A holiday?'

To paint the full picture, I'd better explain that this underfed tribune of the plebs was clad in heavy walking-boots and bright green shorts and had the entire contents of her kitchen in one of those rucksack things strapped to her back. I'd thought the London run of her fresh-air-and-coleslaw show was pretty unwatchable: to catch a matinée in the provinces was like a sneak preview of the sixth circle of Hell. I give you my word I was reeling – and the last time that happened was in 1977 when I was stopped by a lamppost in the Mall after the Chairman of Ways and Means' sixtieth birthday piss-up.

'You're on holiday?' she asked again, a touch of scepticism, it seemed to me, clogging her vocal chords.

'That's the baby,' I said. And it took balls to say this next bit, I can tell you. 'A walking holiday.'

'A *walking* holiday?'

'Yes.'

'You mean –?'

'Yes.'

'Well, well, well.' And like the sun breaking through on a day you'd given up as a non-starter, the most enormous, toothy grin lit up her face. I'd had to make terrible sacrifices to reach the Promised Land, but it was nice to know there was a Promised Land – I'd thought her seriousness was terminal, like the frown on a statue of a bishop. She turned excitedly to her companion.

'Roger, this is John Wellington. From the House.'

'How do you, John.'

'How do you do, Roger.'

'John, this is Roger. My husband.'

'Hullo, Roger.'

'Hullo, John.'

I hadn't really taken in this talking-clock in trousers up to this point. Like the sun and the sky and two-thirds of the Lake District, he'd been hidden from sight by his wife's rucksack. But he sent an immediate chill through me. It was one of those moments when a man feels his hip-pocket to check his wallet is still there.

I don't like knocking people I've only just met, but the kindest way I can describe Roger Bosworth is to say that he looked a worthy consort for the woman he was consorting with. (There's a pithier way of putting that and I'll let you have it when my head clears.) He was quintessentially a thin man. You could have folded his legs and popped them in a matchbox; and from the way they went bone, muscle, bone, muscle from the top of his green woollen socks to the corduroy *cache-sex* which completed the ensemble, you could confidently infer that he'd been going nowhere in a hurry on an exercise-bike when he should have been getting round his meat and two veg. Put him and his missus at one end of a see-saw and me at the other and it would take a medium-sized polar bear in the Bosworth half to get the thing horizontal. Not pretty – and I dare say he thought the same about me.

'You're on a *walking* holiday?' he asked. And again, as with his better half, you got the feeling he was struggling to get his mind round the idea.

'That's it.'

'Do you live around here?'

'No, I'm from London.'

'But you work in the House? With Hilda?'

He was a persistent bugger and the questions showed no sign of letting up. It was like being grilled by a frightfully keen junior counsel on his first case.

'I'm *employed* at the House,' I said, anxious to lighten proceedings. 'But I don't actually work there. I'm a journalist.'

It was one of my very best gags – I've known it reduce my Aunts Amy and Jessica to giggling wrecks over the Christmas turkey. But no joy from Roger Bosworth. He just stared at me with wild incomprehension like one of those dopey villagers in Frankenstein movies.

'I say,' said his wife, with a heartiness which hit me amidships like a Caribbean hurricane. 'We're going up Goat Fell this afternoon. Why not come along?'

'I rather think –'

'It's that one.' She pointed at a vaguely Himalayan object which was blocking out the sun. 'We could be back by tea-time and you'd probably knock off a couple of pounds.'

'Thank you,' I said weakly. 'I'll take a rain-check if you don't mind.' And, feeling as if nothing else in life mattered any more, I staggered back into the Goat and Thistle.

There was no getting round it. The woman had me beaten. Hers wasn't a life of murky secrets and skeletons rattling cupboard doors: it was a clean, healthy, blameless, bloodless thing, lived in the bosom of nature with the squirrels and the hawthorns and the sheep-droppings and the paths for ramblers cut into the hillside. I watched her striding up the fell with Roger, mere specks on the horizon before I'd had three more drinks, and I shuddered with a nameless horror. The House of Commons was big enough for me. It was big enough for her. But it wasn't big enough for both of us.

'. . . and if interest rates go up *again* . . .'

The words came from an old fart in a brown jacket who had parked himself next to me and was conducting what was more or less a monologue with fill-in lines from myself. These rustic ancients can cut up rough if you say nothing at all, so I usually find it easiest to pop in an 'Oh really?' and a 'How interesting', then leg it out to the car when they go to the lav. I was measuring the distance to the door when there was a gap in the conversation which seemed to call for another 'Oh really?' from my side of the net.

'What firm did you say you worked for?' (That's an 'Oh really?' by the way, in case you're getting confused.)

'Harper and Allen. Used to be Harper, Allen and Bosworth. In 1986, when interest rates were . . .'

He sounded as if he was good for another five minutes, ten if I was lucky, so I thought, as I'd done my bit, it was fair game to take a quick kip. My eyes closed slowly, then opened with a start. I don't know if you've found the same, but my brain has a way of cruising along in neutral for hours at a time, then taking off like a greyhound in the slips just when you think it's stalled.

'Did you say Bosworth?' I asked.

'That's it.' The old fart looked startled. He'd obviously made up his mind I was going to be at the non-striker's end till closing time. 'Bosworth.'

'Bosworth?'

'Yes. Bosworth.'

'With a B? And two Os? And a W somewhere in the middle?' I'd had a few by this time.

'Yes, that's it.'

'Nothing to do with Hilda Bosworth by any chance?'

'No, that's the wife. This is Roger Bosworth. He started up the company with the other two, but sold out years ago. He's in a different line of business now. Well, he would be, wouldn't he?'

'Tell me something,' I said, getting none too steadily to my feet. 'You don't mind if I call you Paul, do you?'

'It's Hugh, actually.'

'Well then, tell me something . . . Hugh.' I gestured to the landlord to pour out a couple of doubles and look sharpish. 'What exactly does this company of yours *do*?'

London was looking at its loveliest as I turned into Parliament Square on the Monday morning. Some visiting Pope or President or General Secretary was due in town, so the flags were out and the crowds were building up nicely on the pavement outside the abbey. The sun blazed down, gilding the familiar rooftops. There was a haze over the river, a hint of breeze, a few fleecy clouds chasing each other across the sky and, in my heart, a great peace.

I went down to Annie's for the first one of the day, then wedged myself into one of the telephone kiosks in the corridor leading to the Press Gallery. I meant to enjoy this.

'Three two six three, Hilda Bosworth.'

Even her telephone voice had a dry, starved quality: the ice maiden, in total control of the situation. When I told her I was Dr Felipe Lopez, a visiting nutritionist from Panama City, she was brisk and businesslike.

'What can I do for you, Dr Lopez?'

'I 'ave read your book, Dr Bosworth. *Cholesterol Keells.*'

'Yes?'

'Ees excellent. Vairy, vairy good.'

'Thank you very much.'

'You 'ave 'ad ze courage to take on ze beeg food lobbies and tell zem where zey get off. I am beeg, beeg fan. From Panama City.'

If you're about to say my accent's a bit raw and you've got a Panamanian mother-in-law who talks nothing like this, I don't want to know. It was Monday morning and I was hung over and it fooled the bloody woman, didn't it? Besides, it was the first time I'd tried a Latin medico. My drunken Irishman is a masterpiece and my Ghanaian air attaché has taken in my mother on two separate occasions. These things take practice.

'Dr Bosworth, plees. I ask beeg favour in all humeeleety. Will you 'ave lunch with me today?'

'I don't –'

'I am onlee today and tomorrow in London. It would be beeg honour for me. Maybe you sign my copy of your book?'

'I'm afraid –'

'I am theenking also I want publeesh your book in Panama City. My brother is publeesher, my seester translator. We go feefty-feefty on ze royalties?'

'Well –'

'There would be beeg market in Panama. Everybody talk diet now. A lot of ze small farmers are vairy, vairy unhappy zey are eating so much cholesterol.' And if she believes that one, I remember thinking, she should have a plumber open up her head and straighten a few pipes.

'Very well, Dr Lopez. Can we make it one thirty?'

Si, I said with a fine Panamanian enthusiasm, one thirty would be fine. A little place in Soho perhaps? Just a salad and some fruit and a coffee to finish? And she bought that one too. If the voters of Merryvale had known their MP had the shrewdness of a lobotomised sheep, they would have cut their losses and gone for the sheep.

I returned to Annie's, where Tom was hunched over the crossword.

'You were right, Tom,' I said cordially, always quick to give credit where it's due. 'There *is* dirt on everyone.'

'Whassat?' he asked blankly, for I had disturbed him mid-anagram.

'You said there was dirt on everyone and you were right, my old china. My life, you will be pleased to hear, is no longer a walking misery. I am free. Rejuvenated. Bright-eyed and bushy-tailed. And I'll be standing a round at tea-time, so don't miss it.'

'Aroundyousay?'

He's a bloody good journalist, Tom. Just a bit slow to join the living on a Monday morning, if you know what I mean. He's all right when he's had a couple.

I strode into the restaurant in confident mood.

'The corner table please, Mario. I don't want to be disturbed.'

'Very good, Signor Beef.'

'Bring me a large Scotch and a female called Bosworth when she shows up. Tall, thirtyish, easily mistaken for a strand of spaghetti. She's expecting to have lunch with a Dr Lopez from Panama City. I am Dr Lopez from Panama City. *Capisco*?'

'*Si*, Signor Beef.'

'Good lad.'

I trickled some soda into my Scotch, filled my fist with peanuts and waited for my prey to arrive, which she did at one thirty on the button. From her flushed face, she could have walked all the way from the House, but I didn't believe it – it was the best part of a mile, the last two furlongs uphill. Surely not even this over-energised freak –

'Of all the cheap –' she began, on registering that Dr Lopez of Panama City was none other than your correspondent.

I held up an imperious hand. This was a respectable restaurant. There were publishers, strippers, theatrical agents . . .

'Sit down, Hilda.'

'I've no intention of sitting down.'

'It's better this way, Hilda. The *fettucine* here are fantastic.'

'Better what way? What are you talking about? And if you think I'm eating –'

'It's no good, Hilda, you can't get out of it. Have you tried these *grissini*? They're superb.'

'What's no good? Get out of what? You're talking gibberish.'

'I find, if you take a handful and dip them in a generous amount of butter –'

'I'm not listening to any more of this. I'm off.'

'I wouldn't, Hilda.'

Here the iron beneath the velvet in my voice made itself felt for the first time. She looked me in the eyes, saw I meant business and, with the enthusiasm of a woman summoned to discuss her overdraft with her bank manager after going on a bender in Harvey Nichols, parked herself in the chair opposite.

'What do you want, Mr Wellington?'

'Can we talk about your husband?'

'You mean Roger?'

'Roger.'

'Roger? My husband?'

They have got photographic memories, these politicians. It comes from having so many constituents. She could probably have reeled off the names of her children in chronological order if I'd asked her.

'Roger,' I confirmed, so there could be no doubt we were talking about the same person. 'Between 1973 and 1977, when he sold his interest in the company to the other two, he was the senior partner of Harper, Allen and Bosworth. Does that square with your own recollection?'

'Of course it does.' Her face was white with misery. She knew exactly what was coming.

'Harper and Allen,' I began, at my most professorial (and when I get a chance to be professorial, I grab it, the professorial *persona* being as far removed from my usual soused half-wit as it's possible to imagine) '. . . or, as they then were, Harper, Allen and Bosworth, are the biggest manufacturers of pork pies north of Melton Mowbray. They put between two and three million of the things on the market every month. Now the interesting thing about the British pork pie – stop me if you know this, Hilda, it may be familiar as it's your field – is that it has one of the greatest concentrations of cholesterol of any known foodstuff. The proportion of fat meat to lean meat in its preparation is roughly the same as the proportion of men to women in the House of Commons or, for that matter, of comedians to batsmen in the English cricket team. Furthermore –'

'You've made your point,' she said tartly.

'Furthermore,' I went on, ignoring the intervention, 'you expressly warned people of this fact in your best-selling bodice-ripper *Cholesterol Kills* in which, on page 115 . . .' I fished a copy out of my pocket and turned up the place '. . . no, on page 116, you say and I quote: "Those responsible for flooding our supermarkets with pork pies, cornish pasties and the like have a lot to answer for. These staples of the working-class diet are little better than heart attacks waiting to happen." Close quote.'

'It was just a family joke,' she said weakly, and you had

to feel sorry for the poor ninny. She looked as if she'd just seen her favourite hamster run over by a steam-roller.

'Family joke or not,' I continued sternly, 'it would rather put the skids under your plans to improve the British diet if it was widely known your husband used to be up to his snout in the pork pie trade. Wouldn't it?'

'I suppose so.'

'Well then.'

I left it at that and ordered another drink: it can be thirsty work putting one over somebody like this. The doctor sat there in shell-shocked silence, gnawing the lower lip, picking at the table-cloth, batting the eyelids like nobody's business. When she found her voice, it was barely a whisper.

'I suppose you're going to run this story?'

'Not necessarily. It depends on you.'

'On me?'

'And whether you're prepared to do me a small favour in return.'

'What sort of favour?'

I shall never forget the sheer panic on her face. She had jumped to the conclusion that I was demanding sexual favours and, having stumbled on that dark and dreadful hypothesis, was too thunderstruck to speak. I disillusioned her quickly. I'm a great believer in family values.

'Lay off, Hilda. That's all I'm asking. Live and let live: it's the first rule of parliamentary life. If you see me having a big lunch when you're having a small lunch, say nothing. Just let me get on with it.'

'Yes, but –'

'If you think there's too much of me for my own good, look the other way. Avert your gaze. Turn a blind eye. Pretend I'm not there. Wear sunglasses. Try and see the funny side of it. But *don't* give me any more lectures.'

'All right, but –'

'And *don't* tell me what I should be eating and drinking and what I shouldn't be eating and drinking. I've got a catholic taste in these matters and I want to keep it that way. You're not my doctor, thank God, so get off my back. Understood?'

'If you insist.'

'I do insist. No bullshit from you, no story from me. Simple. And there's one other thing.' I reached for the menu. 'Will you stay and have lunch with me?'

'Why –'

'Because I want you to. We will begin with the *tortelloni della casa*, which is a simple preparation involving butter, double cream, cheese, yolk of egg –'

'I can't –'

'We will follow that with the *truita cacciatore* – that's a plumpish trout cooked in olive oil, garlic, tomato, herbs, mushrooms –'

'How dare –'

'– and then for our main course we will get ourselves round ten-ounce steaks marinated in white wine sauce and served with sauté potatoes, cauliflower cheese, mushrooms *à la Grecque* and double helpings of chips. For dessert I favour the *zabaglione*, although the profiteroles are also good here and it may be necessary to have a selection. We shall then commandeer the cheese trolley –'

'You bastard.'

'– and if you don't want tales of pork pies and Bosworths circulating with tomorrow's cornflakes, you will smile and chirrup and look the giddy goat through the entire proceedings as if we got married last Wednesday.'

'You total bastard.'

It wasn't the matiest lunch I've ever had. A certain amount of ill feeling was apparent and the Bosworth didn't munch her way through the card with quite the verve I had hoped. She picked at the *tortelloni* – there's no other word for it – and barely scratched the surface of the trout. I had to help her finish both courses. But then the atmosphere lightened. She asked if I minded if she had a salad with the steak and, when I generously allowed it, fell on the wretched thing with a longing which made me wonder if I hadn't overdone it. The dessert course was again a little strained but, once I'd asked for the bill and she was sitting there with just a black coffee between herself and freedom, she became almost human. I nearly ambushed her in a smile, although it may have been just a shadow . . .

All this was a few years back. And, in case you're one of those gung-ho types who need a happy ending before they can hit the pillow, you'll be pleased to hear that Hilda and I now get on famously. She's my favourite woman Member by a good length and a half and I suspect, although she'd never admit it, that I'm her favourite lobby correspondent. There's a merriment in the smiles we send winging across the Members Lobby which goes far beyond the call of our professional duties; and, whether or not you could call it affection, we're at least able to view each other's contrasting physiques without reaching for the sickbag.

From time to time we even have lunch together. I don't pretend we eat the same food: miracles like that must await the great Parliament in the skies. But we go our separate ways happily enough – like two golfers hacking their way to the hole down opposite sides of the fairway – and, to my mind at least, our good-humoured acceptance of our differences contains a hint of the magnanimity which is the cornerstone of the parliamentary life.

I hold no brief for people who eat lentils. But I know a good woman when I see one.

7

OUTSIDER ROMPS HOME IN WESTMINSTER CLASSIC

You've probably got hold of the wrong end of the stick by now and decided the House of Commons must be a pretty frivolous institution, run on the same lines as a dormitory feast at St Trinian's or the Harrod's lingerie department on the first day of the Christmas sale.

Far from it.

Last year's November sweep was one of the most tense, solemn, closely fought and, finally, heart-warming events in which I've ever participated. I must have lost two pounds on the last day worrying if Jock would pull it off.

Jock who? Pull what off? I'd better go back to the beginning.

Every November, on the day of the State Opening, the members of something called the P Club meet in the Press Bar at twelve thirty, dip into their wallets and hand over £20 to the club treasurer. There were thirty of us last year, making a pot of £600 which, approximating as it did to a week's credit at the bar, wasn't to be sneezed at. Nor did we sneeze. There was a tension you could cut with a knife as Big Mac, the club secretary, gave the ballot-box a final shake and drew the first name.

'Beef,' he announced. 'Number seven.'

The treasurer looked up the number on the list. 'Number seven – Jock McKibbin.'

At which item of news, I don't mind telling you, my heart fell like a lead balloon. I'd drawn a turkey.

The names being drawn were those of Members of Parliament with a reputation in the House as hell-raisers. Characters who blew their top from time to time and had to be sat on by the Speaker. And the winner of the sweep was the journalist drawing the first Member to be 'named' in the new Session.

'Naming', I should explain, is the House's ultimate sanction against disorderly behaviour. If a Member loses his cool and starts getting fractious, the Speaker appeals to his better nature and tells him to sit down and shut up. If this doesn't work, or he hasn't got a better nature, the Speaker calls out, 'I name Mr Arthur Smith' – which, in a place where everyone calls everyone else 'my Honourable friend' or 'the Right Honourable gentleman', is the last word in insults. The Leader of the House then pops up and says, 'I beg to move that Mr Arthur Smith be suspended from the service of the House' (i.e., chucked out for a week). The House then votes whether to chuck him out. If the Ayes have it, and they generally do have it, off goes Smith for an early bath. Do you get the picture?

The suspense in the Press Gallery as we wait weeks, maybe months, for one of the Members in the sweep to be named is unbearable. It's what keeps us all going in the dog days before Christmas. The trouble was, I just couldn't see Jock McKibbin bringing home the bacon.

Jock's an irascible old bugger. When he flipped his lid in 1976, threw his order paper at the Secretary of State for Scotland and started singing a Gaelic sea shanty during the third reading of the Consolidated Fund Bill, it was acknowledged by all present as a minor masterpiece of parliamentary theatre. But his best days were behind him. Nearer sixty than fifty, he didn't shout and rant and tear his hair with quite the old chutzpah. Sickening to admit, when I'd just drawn him in the sweep, but the man had mellowed. And it's not the mellow ones who get the Speaker dipping into his pocket for the red card.

The ante-post favourites – and lively side-betting adds to the general gaiety – were Mad Mike from Dorset Central, a sort of bearded caveman on steroids, and big Tom McGrath from Humberside, an ex-docker and one of the cussedest so-and-sos who ever forsook an honest living and went into politics. They had been drawn by, respectively, Sam from the *Herald* and BBC new boy Pete Wattle. Bob Mumford had drawn the only mare in the race, Kay Stubbs from Manchester, an 8–1 shot. I'd seen Kay sweating in the paddock and didn't fancy the other two at the prices offered, so I put a tenner on 30–1 outsider Simon Barr-Barker. Simon's a bit slow on his pins these days but, when he blows a fuse, the lights go out all over London – pure pedigree. Then I beetled off to look for Jock.

One of the oldest rules of the P Club is that you can't tell the Member you've drawn in the sweep that you have drawn him. You can egg him on to misbehave and get chucked out; you can talk sweetly and soothingly to his rivals, to make it less likely they will get chucked out. But active collusion is banned.

I voted against this rule when it was introduced, I don't mind admitting, because I'm not really a rules man. Life's a jungle and that's how I like it. But with hindsight it was sensible. There was a Welsh member of the club – called Jones, oddly – who colluded so blatantly he once offered a Cardiff Member £50 to throw a wobbly during the debate on the Queen's Speech. Not cricket. And, propriety apart, if you can persuade a Member to flip but not tell him *why* you want him to flip, it's far more satisfying. You feel – and this is a rare sensation – as if you've done an honest day's work. I remember when I scooped the pool in 1981 by getting Tom Lubbock to call the Chancellor of the Exchequer a two-bit crook because he thought (duff gen from me) that he had undisclosed shares in a South African toiletries company, it was one of the high points of my career.

So it was with due circumspection that I bearded Jock in his lair, a small shoe-box of a room in the Palace cloisters.

'Hullo there, Jock.'

'Hullo, Beef.'

'Keeping well, my friend?'

'Not so bad.'

'Stands Scotland where it did?'

'Ay.'

He gave me what old-fashioned writers call an old-fashioned look. These Scots MPs who've been around since Culloden are canny buggers. When a journalist butters them up, they scratch their sporrans and ask themselves, Why the butter? Add the fact that Jock's room was two hundred yards from the nearest watering-hole, giving my appearance the plausibility of a herd of wildebeests migrating south by south-west across St James's Park, and you'll appreciate that I had my work cut out. I asked him what he thought of the Queen's Speech. He said he hadn't read it yet. I asked how things were in Aberdeen. He said he lived in Inverness. I said weren't they just next to each other. He asked when I was last in Scotland. I asked after his wife. He said she was dead. The conversation lacked fizz, if one was being critical.

'Who's this lovely little lady?' I asked desperately, picking up a photograph of a small girl from his desk. She looked more ghastly than lovely, to be frank, with a touch of foot-and-mouth around the gills but you have to use language creatively in my business. 'Granddaughter?'

'Ay.'

'Three? Three and a half?'

'Four last month.'

'Lovely little thing.'

'Ay, that she is.'

He took the photo from me and gave it the long, loving once over. 'Ay, Beef, that she is,' he repeated, his voice cracking with emotion. 'The loveliest wee girlie you'll ever clap eyes on.'

I shuffled my feet. A Scotsman roused to sentiment is a terrible thing. I remember old Jimmy Dougall showing me a picture of a Glaswegian lass in glasses he'd fallen for in a bad way, and the tears streaming down his cheeks like the Spey in flood. When Jock put his hand on my arm and said, 'Shall I tell you something touching, Beef?', I started remembering urgent appointments in other parts of the building. But some sixth sense made me listen.

'What is it, Jock?'

'She's changed me, Beef,' he went on, in an awed whisper.

'Come again?'

'This wee girlie Janet. She's *changed* me. I'm a new man, Beef. You remember what a wild lad I was? Always shooting my mouth off about things which didn't concern me. Always picking fights when I should have kept mum.'

'I say, look here –'

'You don't have to be polite, Beef. I was. I used to throw my weight about the House as if I owned the place. The way I treated the Speaker was an abomination. Well that's all in the past now – thanks to Janet. She's made me realise –'

'Steady on, Jock, I wouldn't –'

'– that the most important thing in this vale of tears is to be gentle to your fellow man. It took me sixty years to ken that, Beef, but I'm not going to forget it in a hurry.' At which he picked up the photograph and kissed it. Twice.

To say you could have knocked me over with a feather would disregard the laws of physics. No such feather exists. But, if a life insurance salesman had chosen that moment to shove a piece of paper in front of my nose and ask me to sign on the dotted line, he would have done good business. I was so shocked I couldn't think straight. The sight of that rampaging old bull simpering like a choirboy would have tried the patience of St Francis of Assisi – assuming he was patient as well as animal loving, that is, which isn't the sort of thing we bother to check on my paper.

'Jock, it's marvellous to hear you talk like this,' I said, still reeling. 'She must be a remarkable child,' I went on, wishing the fires of Hell would enfold the little blighter. 'But had you thought of the consequences?'

'Consequences?'

'You know what this place is like. A Member has to have
fire in his belly or he's done for. As soon as the other lot
realise that Jock the hell-raiser has become Jock the doting
grandparent, they'll have you for breakfast. You've got a
reputation to protect.'

'The wrong kind of reputation.'

'People used to be terrified of you.'

'I don't want them to be terrified.'

'You were the fieriest speaker in the House.'

'I don't want to be the fieriest speaker in the House.'

'You got up the Speaker's nose like nobody's business.'

'I don't want to get up the Speaker's nose.'

'Couldn't you just combine this gentleness with a bit of
the old oomph? Keep them guessing. Mix it up a bit.
There's no point in being sweetness and light all the time.'

'But I want to be sweetness and light.'

'Not all the time?'

'All the time, Beef. Just like wee Janet. Do you know
what the little angel said to me last Sunday?'

I brought the interview to an end and made for Annie's.
The trainer of a racehorse which had developed Parkinson's
disease on the eve of the big race couldn't have been more
crestfallen. To crown it all, there was Tom McGrath in one
of his filthiest moods.

Tom, you remember, was one of the favourites in the
sweep and had been drawn by Pete Wattle of the BBC, who
was sitting smirking in a corner while Tom let rip. And,
when Tom lets rip, he lets rip. Imagine a large man with a
short temper emerging from a pub on New Year's Eve to
discover that his car's been towed away, his wife's eloped
with the traffic-warden and he's just trod in some dogshit,
and you'll get the general picture. I'd missed the beginning,
but here's an expurgated version of the dénouement.

'. . . bloody Government's the biggest disaster that's ever
happened to this country I'm not bloody putting up with it
I'm going to get up in the House and tell the Prime Minister
these are real people he's fucking about and if the Treasury
don't pull their bloody finger out there'll be blood on the

streets bugger the Speaker bugger Parliament my constituents are pissed off and I'm pissed off and the world's going to know it.'

Strong words, even for Tom. No wonder Pete Wattle was looking so pleased with himself. His horse was raring to go and mine was back in the paddock munching daisies: there was no contest. It was only by some pretty smart footwork that I hung in there.

'Could I have a word, Tom?' I asked smoothly, the second Pete's back was turned. He was a newcomer to the sweep or he would never have left the two of us alone together. Sloppy tactics. He'll learn.

'Go ahead, Beef.'

'I was really interested in what you were saying just now. About the Prime Minister and the Treasury and so on. You want to get it off your chest, don't you?'

'Too bloody right I do.'

'Had you thought of getting the media behind you?'

'What do you mean?'

'If you just make a big scene in the House and get yourself chucked out, you'll grab the headlines for twenty-four hours, then everyone will forget about you. But if you wrote an article in one of the big national papers – a serious, in-depth piece, explaining all your points – people would read what you were saying more carefully and take more notice in the longer term. We pay £500 for articles by big names like you. Think about it, Tom.'

Tom's a bit slow on his feet, so the thinking took a while, but he finally succumbed to the suggestion. I rang my editor, warned him to expect some duff copy and shove it in under the horoscope, and went into the gallery for Questions. Tom was sitting in his place like a lamb, daydreaming about seeing his name in print, and Pete was looking at him in complete confusion, wondering where all that lovely aggro had gone. I was back in the hunt.

But it was a long hard slog. November had passed, then half December, Christmas cards were arriving, turkeys were making their wills – but not a single Member had been chucked out. It was maddening.

I blame the Speaker partly. He had been a schoolteacher before doing time in the House and had the determined benevolence you see in pedagogues of a certain age. He believed in giving people one last chance, then another last chance, then any other last chances they cared to ask for. When Kay Stubbs called the Prime Minister a two-faced crook, and the best he could manage was a 'Tut!' which barely carried to the front benches, a growl of disappointment passed right round the Press Gallery. This wasn't what we'd paid good money to see.

The chances of Jock McKibbin incurring his displeasure looked absolutely hopeless. All that ripe, grandfatherly tolerance I had seen was no accident. It was as if he had abandoned hopes of ministerial office and set his sights on canonisation: there was a quite impregnable piety about the man. Ploy after ploy I tried, to no avail. I even got Mick Ladlow to make a speech to the effect that Scotsmen were unwashed sheep-shaggers who didn't know how to use a knife and fork – ten years back, this would have Jock jumping about like a man with a ferret down his trousers. All he did was chuckle. I could have kicked him to John o'Groats.

Then came the final insult. I was progressing from a Christmas thrash in the Press Bar to a Christmas thrash in the Strangers via a Christmas thrash in the Harcourt Room, hoping if I made good time, to put in some serious drinking in Annie's and maybe squeeze in a bottle of bubbly with my bookmaker, when the division bells started ringing and there was Jock at my elbow with his blasted granddaughter. A smug, curly-haired child of the kind given a bad name by Victorian Christmas cards.

'Do me a favour, could you, Beef? Just look after the wee girlie for five minutes. Bless you.' With which he shot off to vote, leaving me marooned with the child in the Central Lobby, a kind of dentist's waiting-room midway between the two Houses and, more to the point, an alcohol-free zone.

'You,' I said blackly, for I couldn't overlook the disastrous effect this devil's helper was having on her elders and betters, 'must be Janet.'

'Ay.'

'Jock's granddaughter?'

'Ay.'

'Miss Janet McKibbin, from somewhere unpronounceable in the land of the haggis?'

'Ay.'

We left the introductions at that and sat down on one of the green benches to wait: Janet humming 'Twinkle, twinkle, little star', self feeling thirsty and pissed off. Why they don't let children into the division lobbies, I'll never know: it would raise the tone a bit. If that kilted loony Jock thought I was going to –

'Why are you so fat?' enquired a small, polite voice which I eventually traced to my companion.

I ignored the question.

'I said, why are you so fat?'

I ignored that one too.

'You're very fat, aren't you?'

I treated that one with contempt.

'Very, very fat. Why are you very, very fat?'

I maintained an aloof silence.

'Please tell me. Are you sick or do you just eat a lot?'

I judged how hard it was reasonable for a man *in loco parentis* to clout an obstreperous four-year-old round the ear and, not wishing to spoil the ship for a ha'p'orth of tar, clouted her round the ear somewhat harder. She howled, which was the general idea, then carried on howling, which wasn't. It's very hard to judge these things just right. I don't know how parents do it.

Our little *tableau vivant* – Janet howling like a opera singer, self crossing and uncrossing legs, trying to pretend I wasn't with her – drew an audience of about a hundred and fifty adults, none of whom appeared to be smiling. I distinctly heard a voice mutter 'Oh, that poor child', which just goes to show that sympathy for the criminal is running amok at the victim's expense. Of Jock, needless to say, there was not a sign. I was preparing some pretty gamey remarks to greet his return when the sight of Baroness Ffolkes-Caring – a solidly built citizen who had been given her peerage for services to child welfare – heading towards me from a north-westerly direction with a face set to Thundery Showers, persuaded me that a different course was necessary. Scooping the howling brat up in my arms, I force-marched her down to Annie's and, after the necessary pick-me-up for myself, bought her a Kit-Kat and an orange juice. And the howling stopped. Simple, really.

Judging that where I had gone wrong the first time was in allowing junior counsel for the prosecution too many opportunities to press her questions, I took firm charge of the conversation.

'Have you come to London to see Grandpa Jock?'

'Ay.'

'Is he a good grandpa to you?'

'Ay.'

'Does he buy you lots of sweeties and that sort of thing?'

'Ay.'

She was looking at me with suspicion and some distaste. I hadn't thought about it much, but I'd always assumed small children were like dogs: you could clout them one minute, but toss a few biscuits their way and their tails would be wagging the next. They were obviously made of sterner stuff north of the border. Forget nothing, forgive nothing seemed to be this little imp's motto – that and Beware of Strangers with Weight Problems.

'You really are the apple of his eye, aren't you?' I asked, thinking that, if I had an eye and was daft enough to want an apple for it, I'd go for a different tree.

'Ay,' she said smugly. 'Me and the dogs.'

'Dogs?'

'They're collies.'

'Jock keeps collies, does he?' I ordered another drink. My small-talk about dogs can be fitted into a peanut, so I needed reinforcements.

'Ay. Thirteen of them.'

'*Thirteen?*'

That certainly took a bit of getting the brain round and I was just wondering if I had the strength to ask their names and sit through the whole ghastly catalogue, when the man himself burst into the room, swept up Janet in his arms and turned an accusing eye on me. Yes, me. I despair of human nature sometimes.

'Are you out of your mind, Beef, bringing the wee girlie to a place like this? Men drinking whisky at four in the afternoon? So much smoke you can't see where you're going? I've been worried sick looking for the two of you. Worried sick, do you hear? That's the last time I let *you* look after her.'

I had some fruity debating points ready, but he had gone before I could make them and the door was still swinging on its hinges when Tom McGrath burst in and kicked over a stool. I hadn't seen the furniture in Annie's take such a battering since Tiger Hancock got engaged and we overdid the fun and games with the champers bottles.

'I've been looking for you, Beef, you bastard.'

I looked over my shoulder on the off-chance there was another Beef of uncertain parentage in the bar who was expecting a visitor. It was a long shot, but it seemed the only way to avoid having my head knocked off its stand and kicked out of the window, which appeared to be Tom's general game-plan. He was in one his whirling Dervish moods and was clutching a cheque in his hand.

'You said –'

'I'm sure there's a simple explanation, Tom.'

'You said –'

'Let me get you a drink while we talk about it.'

'You said –'

To save my unmarried readers some overcooked Humberside *patois*, I'd better recap in my own words. You remember I offered Tom access to the columns of my organ to vent his spleen on the Government for a fee of five hundred smackers? Well, you know what it's like in Fleet Street.

137

Today's news is tomorrow's fish-and-chip wrapping and, what with one thing and another, when my editor saw Tom's piece, he said he was printing it over his dead body, would only pay up as a favour to me and, if I commissioned any more horseshit, he'd have my waistline for garters. Nor did my ball-park figure of five hundred quid fall in quite the right ball-park. Squinting at Tom's cheque, it looked as if the five had become a two, one of the noughts had dropped off the end and I wasn't sure the other hadn't followed. If ever there was a moment to be economical with the truth, this was it.

'We've had problems in accounts with our new computer, Tom. I'll ring them tomorrow and get it straightened out.'

'I'll get you straightened out if you don't.'

'It's all in hand, Tom.'

'It had bloody better be.'

'Just bear with me.'

'I'm bearing with you.' He prodded my chest, creating a ripple effect down the length of my stomach. 'But I'm not bearing with you much longer. I want to see the article and I want to see the money. Got it?'

'Got it.'

'Good.' And with a snarl, another prod and a dainty pirouette which knocked over a table and sent two chairs flying, he left. I ordered a double and the beginnings of a smile began to play around my lips. I'd cracked the problem.

The following morning, in the paper for which I earn my crust, a small piece appeared on page seven under the head-ing DOG'S LIFE. It was upstaged by the main story – about a Catholic priest overdoing things in the confessional and offering his female parishioners flagellation in the vestry (the boys on the news desk get Christmas bonuses, so they are very inventive in December) – but that didn't matter. I wasn't looking for a large audience.

My piece was short and to the point.

> Junior Home Office Minister Chris Madel upset parents and dog-owners alike in Newcastle-under-Lyme yesterday.
>
> Referring to Home Office proposals for a £10 dog licence, to be introduced on an experimental basis in Scotland, he said, 'Some people are very sentimental about dogs and children. They must keep these things in proportion.'

And, if that doesn't put a firecracker up the old bugger's kilt, I thought as I munched my cornflakes, I'm transferring to the bingo page.

I got into the House with the lark, about half past eleven, and saw Jock striding into the Members' entrance with a cheerful grin on his face. So far, so good. The one danger to my plans was that he would see the story in the morning and blow his top too soon. Luckily my paper is one of the ones with a circulation of two million which nobody actually reads. Someone once suggested we should be given the franchise to supply the House of Commons with bog-roll, but one of the Sundays beat us to it.

Chris Madel button-holed me in the Members Lobby.

'What's all this about me and dog licences, Beef?'

'Just a page-filler, Chris.'

'I've never been near Newcastle-under-Lyme.'

'Of course you haven't.'

'And we're certainly not introducing experimental schemes in Scotland.'

'Of course you're not. Just a page-filler, like I said. News is thin before Christmas.'

He giggled. 'You really are impossible, Beef.' Any other Minister would have hit the stratosphere, but Chris only got his job because his predecessor was foolish enough to roger the Lord Chancellor's secretary at a party conference while I was looking through the keyhole, so he gives me favoured-nation status. I wished him luck for his speech – he was opening the main debate of the afternoon, which was the other reason I'd picked on him – and went up to the Press Bar.

After that everything went according to plan. Prime Minister's Questions was uneventful, there was a statement about the British Rail Pension Fund which anaesthetised anyone who was still standing and, at four thirty, with the House resembling a post-prandial gathering at an old people's home, the Speaker left the Chair and was replaced by his deputy. This was good news from my point of view for, if the Speaker at that time erred on the side of leniency, his deputy was a quick-tempered, mouth-frothing ex-brigadier who took no nonsense from anyone, particularly Scots playing silly buggers.

The next debate was entitled the Crisis in Her Majesty's Prisons. Opposition Members were upset because prisons were overcrowded or it may have been undercrowded and their home affairs spokesman made a lively knockabout speech which, judging by the hyena-noises, everyone enjoyed. Chris Madel rose to reply for the Government, at which point a small brown envelope could be seen passing along the Opposition benches to Jock.

Up to now, his manner had been one of unimpeachable serenity. He sat with the air of a man listening to his favourite symphony, swaying his head to and fro in time with the music and strumming his fingers on his knee. His eyes were half shut and he must have been nodding off because, when the envelope reached him, his neighbour had to nudge him twice to catch his attention. He sat up, opened the envelope and out popped my article with the words DID YOU SEE THIS? added in my fair hand – and that was the last anyone saw of Jock's serenity for about three and a half weeks.

It's very hard to convey to anyone who wasn't there the sheer magnitude of the eruption. It was as if all that mellowness, all that serenity, had been covering a nuclear warhead which someone had decided to detonate. Similar phenomena, I imagine, would have been observed by someone playing golf at the Krakatoa Country Club in 1883 and noticing, as he holed out at the seventh, that the day was clouding over. You probably think I'm exaggerating. I'm not. I was there.

The following day's Hansard doesn't capture the true flavour of the exchanges, but it gives the sequence of events accurately.

MR CHRISTOPHER MADEL:	... and, with the anticipated acceleration in the Government's prison-building programme, the indications are that by 1992–93 ...
MR JOCK MCKIBBIN:	Will the Minister give way?
MR CHRISTOPHER MADEL:	If the Honourable Member will allow me to complete the point I was making –
MR JOCK MCKIBBIN:	Will the Minister give way?
MR CHRISTOPHER MADEL:	By 1992–93, if present trends continue and –
MR JOCK MCKIBBIN:	I have something important to say to the Minister.
MR DEPUTY SPEAKER:	Order. The Minister is not giving way. The Honourable Member must resume his seat.
HON MEMBERS:	Sit down, Jock.
MR JOCK MCKIBBIN:	On a point of order, Mr Deputy Speaker. The Minister cannot be allowed to continue his speech until he has accounted for the outrageous, evil remarks he made in Newcastle-under-Lyme yesterday. Decent-minded people will be appalled that a Minister of the Crown should say such things. I don't think –
MR DEPUTY SPEAKER:	Order. Order. This is not a matter for the Chair.
MR JOCK MCKIBBIN:	I don't think I can ever remember such a shocking disregard for human feeling.
HON MEMBERS:	He's been at the hooch again.

MR DEPUTY SPEAKER:	Order. The Honourable Member must resume his seat when I am speaking. He is not making a genuine point of order and the Minister has not given way. Mr Christopher Madel.
MR CHRISTOPHER MADEL:	Thank you, Mr Deputy Speaker. If it is of any assistance to the Honourable gentleman –
MR JOCK MCKIBBIN:	Will the Minister give way?
MR CHRISTOPHER MADEL:	I believe I can clarify –
MR JOCK MCKIBBIN:	Will the Minister stop interrupting and allow me to make my point?
MR DEPUTY SPEAKER:	Order. Order. The Minister has the floor. The Honourable Member must restrain himself.
MR JOCK MCKIBBIN:	On a point of order, Mr Deputy Speaker. It is quite intolerable that the Minister should receive the attention of the House at a time like this. He has acted disgracefully and offended all reasonable people. His remarks make it quite clear that he's a heartless, hypocritical *******.
MR DEPUTY SPEAKER:	Order. Order. Did the Honourable Member say *******? I must ask him to withdraw that word immediately.
MR JOCK MCKIBBIN:	I said ******* and I meant *******.
HON MEMBERS:	Withdraw! Withdraw!
MR DEPUTY SPEAKER:	Order. I am warning the Honourable Member very seriously. He has been in the House long enough to know that we cannot tolerate language of that sort.

	If he doesn't withdraw the word ******* now –
HON MEMBERS:	Chuck him out.
MR JOCK MCKIBBIN:	I've no intention of withdrawing, Mr Deputy Speaker. The Minister has only himself to blame. He's not just a *******, he's a **** and a son of a ******.
HON MEMBERS:	Disgraceful!
MR DEPUTY SPEAKER:	Order. Order! The Honourable Member's conduct is quite intolerable. I name Mr Jock McKibbin.

At which point, with the House in uproar and Jock being bundled out of the Chamber screaming crisp one-liners about Sassenachs, a grin of substantial proportions could be observed on my face. The media are often accused of trivialising politics but, when things get serious, we know how to conduct ourselves.

'I don't know how you dream these things up, Beef,' said Sam Barber admiringly as he handed over the six hundred smackers in the bar in front of the assembled P Club. 'The rest of us had given up for Christmas and you were still in there fighting.'

'Psychology and timing,' I said. 'That and a bit of luck. I knew old Jock had it in him somewhere. It was just a question of pressing the right buttons at the right time. Twenty-seven doubles when you're ready, Reg.'

'I couldn't do that sort of thing on my paper,' said Bob Mumford ruefully. 'Our stories have to be checked.' (Bob writes for those Sunday heavies which make such good dustbin-liners. Nice man, writes poetry in his spare time.) I would have taken issue but, when you've scooped the pool, you can afford to be magnanimous, so I nodded sagely.

'I really thought I had a chance,' said Pete Wattle. 'My man just went off the boil completely. I can't make it out.'

I nearly choked on my drink: I'd completely forgotten stage two of my plan. At the first lull in the festivities, I slipped out of the bar and headed for the message-board in the Members Lobby. In Chris Madel's pigeon-hole I popped a note apologising for landing him in the brown stuff and offering lunch at a restaurant of his choice; in Tom McGrath's an envelope containing £200 of my hard-won loot (I hated parting with it, but it was easier than making out my will and booking undertakers) and a letter in these terms:

Dear Tom,

The computer problem in accounts is worse than any-one realised, but I've been authorised to pay you in cash as you're such a valued contributor. [Tom has a nose for lots of things, but not irony.] Slightly less than advertised, I'm afraid, but I think when you see how well your material comes across – we're running it tomorrow – you'll be more than satisfied.

You may find the packaging a bit unorthodox, but we're not a conventional paper and this is Christmas week – you've got to pull out all the stops to catch people's attention.

Seasons greetings,
Beef

Having done the necessary, I returned to the orgy in the Press Bar. The first stretcher-case collapsed just before midnight, after which they dropped like flies.

The following morning, even the news that a member of the Royal Family had sprained a muscle shopping in Harrod's – with which our rivals led – had to take second place to a Beef Wellington exclusive blazoned across the front page.

MP IN AMAZING XMAS PROTEST
The Government's economic policies came under savage attack last night – from an MP dressed as Father Christmas.

> Humberside's Tom McGrath astonished passers-by in Whitehall by getting out of a taxi in full Santa Claus costume and presenting a petition at 10 Downing Street.
>
> 'I want to draw public attention to what my constituents have suffered under this Government,' said 54-year-old Tom, removing his beard to address a crowd of onlookers.
>
> 'The Chancellor of the Exchequer must go. The Prime Minister must go. Then perhaps we will have a Government which cares about ordinary people.'
>
> Later ex-docker Tom led the crowd in singing 'Good King Wenceslas' and 'Away in a Manger'.

There was bad blood between Tom and me for a while after that, indeed he threatened to do various energetic things with my insides when the House got back after Christmas. But when an opinion poll in his local paper showed that he was likely to double his majority as a result of my story, he relented mightily and rang to apologise.

To complete the story, I should explain that the editor of his local paper is an old friend of mine and hadn't actually consulted the populace before publishing the poll. I like to think my paper sets the standards, but there are some very professional journalists in the provinces.

8

NIGHT IN LIFT HORROR

From a superficial reading of these little narratives, you may have got the impression that I have an innate hostility towards politicians and my heart's desire is to see them thrashing about in the soup. The reality is more complex.

It's true that a Government Minister sitting at his desk getting quietly on with his job is about as newsworthy as a mother of two in Chipping Camden with a C reg Ford Escort and a diminished sex drive. Let him frequent massage parlours and opium dens if he wants to carry clout at my end of Fleet Street. But there are plenty of decent, hard-working, middle-of-the-road Ministers with whom I'm on perfectly good terms and whom I'm quite happy, provided they leak like sieves, to see hold their portfolios indefinitely. I'll even do them small personal favours.

Take the strange case of the Red Box, the Domestic Crisis and the French Buffet Car.

I was taking the lift down from the Press Bar to the ground floor at the end of a hard day's work when Bernard Calder, the Transport Secretary, got in. He said 'Hullo, Beef,' I said 'Hullo, Bernard,' and, as we only had one floor to go, it was going to be 'Goodnight, Beef,' 'Goodnight, Bernard,' and home to our respective beds. One of those neat, symmetrical conversations which leave you feeling all's well with the world and, if only everyone observed the simple courtesies, there would be no need for politicians or, for that matter, journalists.

Halfway between the mezzanine floor and the ground, the lift shuddered to a halt. I pressed various buttons, but it wouldn't budge. The emergency telephone was broken and attention shifted, with a kind of grim inevitability, to a sign reading MAXIMUM LOAD 5 PERSONS OR 375 KG. Bernard shot me an accusing look. He was the bluff, soldierly type with a bit of a reputation for intolerance.

'If I'm seventy-five kilos, what are you?'

I was shocked. Genuinely shocked. 'Bernard, really. You can't just ask a man's weight like that.'

'Why not?'

'I don't see that it's any of your business.'

'It is if we're stuck in a lift together and I'm in a hurry to get home. Come on, what's the damage?'

'I resent that remark,' I said stiffly. 'My body is in no sense damaged. It is a thing of dignity and authority and I carry it with pride. On the matter of weight, the facts are uncertain. I don't understand these new-fangled French measurements, but on the old imperial scale I answer to twenty-two stone.'

'Christ almighty.'

'That figure goes back to 1986 when I was put on a machine for weighing livestock at Simon Grove's farm, by way of post-lunch entertainment for the assembled company. The machine had been doctored to get more money out of the EEC, so the reading may have been on the low side. You also have to remember that in 1987 I went through a phase of eating T-bone steaks for breakfast –'

'Oh Jesus.'

'– and that in 1989 I found I slept better if I had a large cognac in the bath and took a couple of Mars bars to bed with me. But, Bernard,' I went on quickly, seeing him turn a nasty shade of green, 'all this is irrelevant. The fact is that I was in the lift first and, if you didn't fancy your chances of completing the journey safely, you shouldn't have got in with me. Enough of this idle arithmetic. Let's do some

148

positive thinking. I'm not saying this sort of thing happens to me all the time but, in my experience, the essential thing when you're stuck in a lift is to remain on good terms with your fellow prisoner and let the outside world know what's happening. Are you ready? On the count of three.'

We filled our lungs and gave it everything we had.

'HELP!'

'Once more with feeling.'

'HELP! HELP!'

'And a third time. Hit that top C with a bang.'

'HELP! HELP! HELP!'

For men of middle years it was a magnificent effort, though I say it myself. You could have heard us in the House of Lords. We relaxed and looked at each other. Bernard smiled for the first time. Not long now, you could see him thinking, not long now . . .

Two and a half hours later, the mood could no longer be called sanguine. Nobody had come to our rescue because they had all gone home to bed. Also, this lift was only four foot square, which meant we rubbed against each other rather: I've known newly married couples enjoy less body-contact. This agitated Bernard mightily and he was a shade graceless, it seemed to me, in conveying the impression that, if he'd been asked to describe his biggest nightmare, spending the night in a lift with me would have topped the poll.

'You know what I really hate about this?' he grumbled. 'Not being near a whisky bottle. I lay off the stuff during the day but, when I get home at night, I have a couple of glasses and the world seems a whole lot more sane. Are you with me?'

'Yes and no. Nightcaps I'm familiar with: laying off the stuff during the day is foreign territory. Wait a minute,' I said slyly. 'I think I may have just what the doctor ordered.'

This may seem pretty obvious, but one of the things about having ample hips is that you have ample hip-pockets; and ample hip-pockets can accommodate even ampler hip-flasks. When Bernard saw the generous cargo of Scotch I was carrying, his face lit up like a fruit-machine.

'Beef, you old devil!'

'Regulation issue,' I said modestly. 'You won't find a reporter on my paper without one. Drink deep, my friend. We've got a long night ahead of us.'

He took the flask, filled up the tank and gave a beatific smile.

'God, I needed that.'

'Good, isn't it?'

'Bloody marvellous.'

'I don't go much for Jocks as a general rule, but you've got to admire the way they recycle their tap-water.'

'Too bloody right. Fancy a cigarette, Beef?'

'Have one of mine, Bernard.'

'Thanks, Beef, I don't mind if I do.'

We lit up and before long our prison cell, which had seemed such a cold, friendless place, was an earthly paradise perfumed with the bouquet of Rothmans and Johnnie Walker. I loosened my tie and Bernard did the same. He took another gulp from the flask and smiled. Beneath the Ministerial bluster, he was a kind man, the sort you couldn't help liking.

'I'm sorry I was a bit short with you earlier, Beef.'

'Quite all right, Bernard.'

'No, it's not quite all right. Can I have another swig?'

'Please do.'

'It's never right to talk to someone like that. It was bloody personal and it was out of order. Apologies.'

'Accepted.'

'The fact is, Beef – Christ, this stuff is good – the fact is that you're not by any stretch of the imagination a fat man. Not by a mile. To call you fat would be a travesty of the facts.'

'Are you feeling all right, Bernard?'

'Absolutely fine, Beef. You're overweight, of course, but then we're all overweight, aren't we? But fat? Fat? Not a bit of it. I see men like you in my constituency every week and the question of fatness simply doesn't enter into it. May I?'

'Help yourself.'

'What I'm really trying to say, Beef, is that I just wouldn't call a man like you fat. Or even obese. Never. And that's not being polite. I'd probably say – I never touch this stuff during the day, you know – I'd probably say you were well built. Well built. Like a Regency house. If a storm blows up, you're not going to be knocked over for want of ballast. You're made to last, Beef.'

'Thanks, Bernard, I appreciate that.'

'I say, do you mind if we sit down? I'm feeling a bit faint.'

The one thing every schoolboy knows about lifts is that they're designed to carry passengers vertically, not horizontally. Bernard and I hadn't been too comfortable standing up: when we tried to stretch ourselves out on the floor, it involved the sort of contortions people shrink from in the final throes of sexual ecstasy. He wriggled, I wriggled, we both thrust down with our thighs; when we finally hit bottom, my knee was up against his kidneys and his mouth was six inches from my ear. If ever there was a moment for an off-the-record briefing . . .

'Shall I let you into a little secret, Beef?'

I knew it. The hooch, the tobacco, the rubbing shoulders – they loosen a man's tongue something rotten.

'Fire away, Bernard.'

'You won't tell anyone?'

'Not a living soul.'

'You mean that? Not a living soul?'

'My word as a journalist.'

'All right then. You see, the thing is, Beef – I say, you don't have any more of that stuff, do you?'

'All yours, Bernard.'

'Much obliged, Beef. I shan't forget this in a hurry. Sublime stuff, isn't it? They make it in places called distilleries. Did you know that? I visited one near Edinburgh when I was Minister of Agriculture. Some promotional stunt or other. Did I tell you my little secret, by the way?'

'You were just getting to the punch-line.'

'Was I? God, my mind wanders sometimes. It must be the lights. The thing is, Beef – I'm about to be sacked.'

I sat up with a jolt. 'Given the push, eh?' When a man's knocking off your emergency rations like a sailor just off ship, you're entitled to expect a decent divi in the way of gossip. But this was riches indeed.

'Exactly, Beef. Couldn't have put it better myself. Given the push. Shown the door. Handed the pink slip. Asked for my portfolio. Five years in the Cabinet working my arse off for that bloody man and he says it's time I made way for someone younger. Younger, my eye. I'm fifty-two, Beef. The prime of life. You don't think I'm over the hill, do you?'

The question called for a diplomatic answer. In the back row of every Cabinet photo you will see men of unswerving loyalty coupled with a complete lack of imagination. Such a man was Bernard Calder. Hardworking, certainly. Well-meaning, I grant you. But you could put a conductor on an eighty-eight bus in his place and the affairs of state would go on unchanged. When he asked if he was over the hill, he was trifling with the facts. He'd never been up the hill.

'You're as good at your job as ever,' I said smoothly, taking advantage of the lull in the conversation to retrieve my hip-flask. A slightly sozzled Cabinet Minister suited me fine. I wanted to avoid having a slightly unconscious Cabinet Minister.

He gave a lop-sided grin. 'Thanks, Beef. That's big of you. I've been a bloody good Secretary of State for Transport, haven't I?'

'You've been your own man, Bernard.'

'When have I ever cocked anything up?'

'You've set standards and followed them.'

'When did I ever let the side down?'

'There's nobody like you.'

'Exactly. Five years in Cabinet toeing the party line, voting the right way, sticking up for colleagues, keeping my nose clean, working till I dropped, never missing a meeting, never putting a foot wrong, telling the Prime Minister he was doing the right thing and there was no alternative and the voters loved his cotton socks and all that crap – and what happens? The little shit asks me into his office this afternoon and says he wants me to go in the next reshuffle. The next reshuffle! That's next week, Beef. What am I going to tell Heather? What am I going to tell the girls? How am I going to look people in the face in the Tea Room? Oh Beef, Beef, Beef!'

There was no escaping the fact that the Right Hon Member for Greater Northampton was crying like a baby. Bucketfuls of the stuff. I've seen more self-control from French actresses. I tut-tutted and patted him on the arm, but this just spurred him to fresh torrents.

'And do you know what?' he sobbed. 'Do you know what? Who do you think he's planning to put in my place? Go on, have a guess. Think of the most unlikely, unsuitable, unprepossessing person imaginable and you've got it in one.'

'Ginger Hobbs?'

'No.'

'Simon Barr-Barker?'

'Warm.'

'The mad dwarf of Basingstoke?'

'Very warm. Shall I tell?'

'Tell away.'

'Matthew Robb.'

'He isn't.'

'He is.'

'That short-arsed twerp with the specs and the teeth he's borrowed from his granny?'

'That same short-arsed twerp.'

'My poor dear friend,' I said, putting my arm round his shoulder and re-submitting the hip-flask, 'this is frightful. It reminds me of a Greek tragedy I was taken to at school where the hero was tied to a rock and didn't see the funny side of things at all.' And, if I hadn't had such an iron constitution, I would probably have had a quiet blub myself.

This Matthew Robb – Bernard's deputy at the Department of Transport – was far and away the most intelligent Member of the House. If Bernard belonged to the bus conductor school, he represented the Nobel Prize tendency. There was a lump on the top of his head as if he'd been brained with a baseball bat. You'd have thought his unsuitability for high political office would have been obvious. Look at the facts. What have the six most incompetent Ministers since the war got in common? A first-class degree at Oxford. And the six most competent? Two O-levels and the ability to walk into a fish and chip shop as if they owned it. I reminded Bernard of these statistics and he nodded sombrely.

'Exactly. Totally unsuitable. I wouldn't mind handing over the steering-wheel to someone with a bit of nous, but Robb's just not part of the real world. Did you know he reads *The Times Literary Supplement*?'

'He doesn't.'

'He does. I saw him in the Tea Room last week. I'm sorry, Beef, I'm just going to have to get a long rope and top myself. I can't stand it. I really can't.'

And without so much as a 'Have you set the alarm-clock, darling?', he had rolled over and fallen asleep. First confessions from the heart, then weeping attacks, now loud snoring noises: I've known Scotch do strange things to a man, but I've never seen it pull quite so many tricks at one sitting.

I was thinking about a spot of shut-eye myself when, tucked under the Right Honourable Member's elbow, I noticed a bright red dispatch-box with the House of Commons portcullis engraved on the top. You see Ministers swanking round the place with these things and they are reputed to contain more juicy titbits than a laundry-basket in a Turkish harem. As Bernard was now snoring like the horns section of the London Philharmonic, I opened the box and, before you could say section two of the Official Secrets Act, had settled down to read the contents.

I don't think I've ever been so disappointed in my life.

Page after page was written in a Civil Service *patois* so different from our house style that the problems of translation seemed insuperable. '*Resolved*, That the sub-Committee stand adjourned till Thursday next.' Little crackers like that. My pulse did quicken when I picked up the minutes of a recent Cabinet meeting; but without the benefit of stage-directions like '(*Chancellor of the Exchequer blushes*)' or '(*Fur really flying now*)', they read like the proceedings of a parish council.

And the amount of figures: 9.4 per cent, 3.1 per cent, 6.75 per cent over eighteen months. I'd no idea Ministers had to get their brains round such stuff. It confirmed my deepest prejudices about economics – a subject on which I've held trenchant views since the time a Hungarian egghead announced there was no such thing as a free lunch. Bull's blood. There was a month in 1983 when I didn't have to pay for a single coffee.

Half an hour's browsing and, if I'd had a Dick Francis in my pocket, I would have swopped with enthusiasm. Then my eye was caught by a tiny one-page memorandum in the very last file . . .

Bernard woke with a violent start at six o'clock in the morning.

'WherethehellamI?'

I appraised him of the facts.

'HowlonghaveIbeenasleep?'

I gave a conservative estimate.

He clutched his head in his hands. 'God, I feel *terrible*.' He caught sight of the flask and groaned. 'What is that stuff? Weedkiller?'

'Ordinary Scotch with a small infusion of *grappa*. It's the *grappa* that gives it its kick. I got the recipe from Ginger Hobbs. He says it makes respectable women forget their upbringing completely.'

'My head feels as if it's about to explode. What happened? Did I say anything embarrassing?'

'Not in the slightest. We just talked.'

'What about? I don't remember talking. You'll be telling me next I got smashed and let you in on all sorts of state secrets. I suppose I told you about . . .' He stopped and stared at me. 'My God, I *did* tell you.'

I nodded gravely. 'You did, Bernard. The whole squalid story. And pretty depressing it was. The thought of that stick-insect Robb having a seat in Cabinet is still giving me a queasy feeling in the stomach. Profoundest sympathies and so on.'

'Thanks, Beef. That's kind.'

'If old muckers like you are going to be put out to grass to make room for that sort of tick, we're living in dangerous times. The next thing you know they'll make an accountant Archbishop of Canterbury. He is an accountant? I didn't know. There's no time to be lost, Bernard. We must stop this wicked thing happening.'

'How can we possibly stop it? The PM's made his mind up. He's announcing it next week.'

'Monday?'

'Wednesday.'

'Then we're in with a shout. The tabloid press is still a force in the land and I'm going to prove it. Are you a betting man, Bernard?'

'I have the odd flutter.'

'Then flutter along to the nearest bookmaker and put a tenner on Matthew Robb ending his days sewing mail-bags in Wormwood Scrubs while you reside in splendour at No 10 Downing Street. They'll give you 66–1. The only other thing you need to do –'

'What are you going to do?'

I put my finger to my lips. 'Journalists move in mysterious ways, their wonders to perform. You will see strangely worded articles by me in the next few days which will have you hopping about like a blue-arsed fly. But trust me, Bernard. I'm on your side and we're winning. You must do just one thing. That announcement about the Anglo-French rail consortium you're due to make on Thursday.'

He boggled. 'How did you know about that? It's supposed to be top secret.'

'No longer, I fear. They're talking about it freely in my local laundromat. The point is, Bernard, you're not to make the announcement yourself. Let Robb deputise for you.'

'And take all the credit? Are you mad? That deal's creating two and a half thousand British jobs. It's an absolute winner. We haven't stuffed the French like that round the negotiating table since the Battle of Waterloo.'

'Be that as it may. Don't touch the thing with a bargepole. I look in the crystal ball and see restless natives. Let Robb handle it.'

'If you insist, Beef.'

'I do insist. And now,' I said, levering myself to my feet. 'It's seven in the morning and, if we give it everything we've got, there should be a cleaning woman within earshot. All together now.'

'HELP!'

'Once more, in the key of F.'

'HELP! HELP!'

Ten minutes later, we were standing in the rain in New Palace Yard waiting for a taxi. The red box stood chastely by Bernard's side. He looked at it and chuckled.

'To think I had that little lot with me and fell asleep in the company of a journalist. You missed the boat, Beef.'

'That's life, Bernard.'

'You could have read the lot, Beef.'

'You win some, you lose some, Bernard.'

And I looked at him and thought, not without tenderness: we *need* men like Bernard in the Cabinet; the whole system depends on them. Without generous co-operation from Members of Parliament, how can you have government by the media for the media?

The next morning, page six of my paper carried the following items:

(1) TWENTY THINGS YOU DIDNT KNOW ABOUT KYLIE MINOGUE;
(2) I MARRIED A SEX FIEND;
(3) GAY PRIEST'S AIDS CLANGER; and
(4) ROBB FOR CABINET?

Anyone sick, depraved or short-sighted who read item (4) before the others would have their dirty little minds gratified with the following:

> Matthew Robb has been reliably tipped as the new Transport Secretary in next week's reshuffle.
> He will replace Bernard Calder whose life has been rocked by a domestic crisis.
> Robb caught the PM's eye with his slick handling of the Anglo-French rail deal. He is 39.

Within five minutes of the paper landing on my door-mat, Bernard was on the telephone. I had said he would be hopping about like a blue-arsed fly, but I doubt if the bluest-arsed fly could have shown such nifty footwork.

'I haven't had a domestic crisis in my life, Beef. Heather and I are like Romeo and Juliet. We've got the best marriage in the House and everyone knows it. People despise us we're so happy. If you don't print an apology on the front page tomorrow –'

'Calm yourself, Bernard.'

'I've no intention of calming myself. It's bad enough getting the push without having your private life dragged through the mud. Heather's a very sensitive woman. She's a management consultant. And giving Robb the credit for the French deal! He couldn't have pulled that off if he'd spent twenty years trying. He's hopeless with the Frogs. He can't even say "*Où est le* night-life?" I'm warning you, Beef –'

'Bernard listen –'

'I won't listen.'

'You will listen. These are deep waters and we must negotiate them with care. As regards your domestic circumstances, I plead guilty to a slight exaggeration. I know of your love-nest with Heather and may a thousand flowers bloom for you. But, Bernard, we're not reporting news, but trying to influence events. Imagine you are the Prime Minister poised to stab an old colleague in the back. Your dagger is drawn, you have selected your spot between the shoulder-blades, you have steeled yourself to administer the *coup de grâce*. Then, just as you are about to strike, you realise that your victim is tormented by a secret sorrow. What do you do?'

'Ah.'

'Do you strike or do you hesitate?'

'Ah.'

'You never spoke a truer word. Ah, if I may say so, is a masterly summary of the position. Just keep looking as if you've been rocked by an unspecified domestic crisis and, if you don't feel the warm blast of sympathy from No 10, I'm a Dutchman. As for Robb –'

'Hang Robb.'

'I intend to. The gallows are waiting. Have you arranged for him to make the statement this afternoon?'

'Yes, I'm in Birmingham. But I really don't see –'

'You will, Bernard. Now can I finish my breakfast, please? I've got important work to do.'

Sir John Bull, whom I tracked down in Annie's, is one of those elderly, patriotic types whose life ends at Dover and whose subconscious is racked by a terror of all things Continental. Other men have nightmares about falling from great heights or rising to address a Women's Institute meeting and discovering that their trousers are at half-mast. Sir John dreams of being chased down the Channel Tunnel by Belgian bureaucrats brandishing EEC directives. Say Brussels and his nose twitches like a rabbit's. Say 1992 and molten lava streams from his mouth.

'*Bonjour, mon brave*,' I said, shaking hands. Sir John prepares for Armageddon by pretending the whole thing's a joke, so this sort of horse-play amuses him.

'*Bonjour, Monsieur Beef.*'

'*Ça va?*'

159

'*Ça va* bloody awful. What are you having, you daft bugger?'

'The usual please, Jack.'

'When you're ready, George. What's up, Beef? You're looking like something out of a horror film.'

'I'm upset, Jack. This business with Bernard Calder is too bad.'

'I thought you hacks liked Ministers getting the boot. It sells newspapers, doesn't it?'

'Bernard's the exception which proves the rule. He's a decent bloke. I've spent the night in a lift with him. I know his qualities.'

He gave me an odd look. 'To each his own, I suppose. You know why he's for the high jump, don't you?'

'Hand in the till?'

'Don't be silly. He's too bloody European for his own good and the Prime Minister's had enough. Sucking up to the Frogs like that, I ask you. The next thing you know we'll have charcuterie shops on Ealing High Street.'

'Be fair, Jack. This rail consortium's good news, isn't it?'

'I'll believe it when I see it. They haven't announced the details yet. High treason, I call it.'

'Anyway, Bernard's not responsible for that. It's Robb's show.'

'Matthew Robb dreamed that one up? I don't believe you. He's one of us.'

'He may be one of us, but he knows a good thing when he sees one. There is one odd thing about the deal, though. Shall I tell you?'

'I can't wait.'

I divulged the small, lethal fact which had caught my eye in the memorandum marked SECRET – IN STRICTEST CONFIDENCE in Bernard's red box. Sir John went purple in the face and said I couldn't be serious. I said I could be serious. He said, if Robb thought he could get away with that, he was an arrogant little shit. I said I hated knocking politicians but I was inclined to agree. At which Sir John had a mild coronary, knocked back his brandy and, with the

160

words 'They won't stand for this in Ealing' ringing round the bar, charged upstairs to the Chamber.

Matthew Robb sat coolly by the dispatch-box waiting for the Speaker to call him. When you've got a brain the size of Battersea power station, it does give you a certain self-confidence and, if anything, he was looking even brainier and cockier than usual.

The reason for his chirpiness wasn't far to seek. Bernard had described the rail consortium as the best Anglo-French fixture since the Battle of Waterloo and he had not exaggerated. Members' mouths dropped open in disbelief as Robb announced the details. The concept was a bit bizarre – a jointly funded high speed rail-link between London and Paris – but the financial pluses and minuses were breathtaking. Total French investment: £13 billion. Total British investment: £1.7 billion. Total British jobs created: 2,500. Total French jobs created: 137. The Opposition spokesman on transport was left speechless. He gritted his teeth, said thank God the Government had got something right for a change and sat down. Various other Members got to their feet.

'Sir John Bull!' called the Speaker.

The purpleness which I had brought to that fine old face was still in evidence. His moustache bristled, his shoulders heaved, his voice trembled with emotion. He sounded like an Old Testament prophet denouncing the tribes of Israel.

'Can the Minister confirm,' he thundered, 'that the catering on this new rail-link is to be done under contract by a *French* firm?'

There were rumbles of interest. Robb consulted his brief.

'And could he explain,' Sir John went on, 'why we yet again have to endure the spectacle of a British Minister standing at the dispatch-box and telling the House he's sold his country down the river?'

The carriage trade below the gangway stirred in their seats. Anything involving selling down the river is big box-office. Robb got smoothly to his feet. The vultures were gathering, but he hadn't seen them.

'The answer to my Honourable friend's first question is yes,' he said. 'Catering on the Green Arrow will be undertaken by a French firm. This was a small concession which was economically insignificant in the context of the whole package. But I reject the assumption behind his second question. There needs to be some give-and-take in international relations and, in view of France's high culinary reputation –'

The storm broke. I don't know if you've ever seen a Siberian peasant set on by a pack of wolves and torn limb from limb? Probably not, unless you have Russian in-laws. My point is that Matthew Robb's fate in the next half-hour was to play the peasant's part in the scenario I've described. There are times when Ministers escape with a flesh wound and times when they get mauled. Robb was mauled.

A Minister of average intelligence would have coped just fine, for the thing about not knowing all the answers is that it conditions you to survive in a hostile environment. I must have seen Bernard at the dispatch-box dozens of times, flannelling away, ducking questions, losing his temper, saying he'd take things on board and the Honourable Member had raised a valid point and this wasn't a party issue – all the old gags. But at the end of the day he always achieves his objective, which is to get through the questions without promising to spend any more money. A real pro.

Robb's case was different. He was a man of high intelligence and could do arithmetic in his head. The catering contract was such obviously small beer compared with the total package that anyone with any grasp of economics would realise the fact. He reiterated this point about a dozen times, at first patiently, then with increasing testiness. But it was wasted on his audience. He wasn't addressing the London Business School, but the House of Commons in full cry. And if there's one thing dear to a backbencher's heart, it's British Rail tea and British Rail sandwiches. Suggest substituting *le café complet* and *le brioche* and you have a riot on your hands. When Robb in desperation made an appeal to the spirit of the Treaty of Rome, the howls of derision were so loud the Speaker had to call for order.

The Prime Minister was sitting next to Robb on the front bench and the look on his face said it all. He had always admired Robb for what he called his hinterland – reading novels, going to Covent Garden, that sort of thing – but he was learning a bitter lesson. You can have a hinterland the size of Wales but, when the wolves are tearing you limb from limb, it doesn't do much good. It's the hinterland they go for first.

Bob Mumford was at my elbow, relishing the blood-letting. 'Do you know why Calder's not making this statement himself?' he whispered.

'He's in Birmingham.'

'He's well out of this little lot.'

'Isn't he just? A smart man, Bernard Calder. Knows when to take advice.'

Bob eyed me suspiciously. 'What do you mean, advice? You haven't pulled another fast one, have you?'

'My lips are sealed, Bob.'

'You bastard.'

'And a happy Christmas to you.'

After the statement, when Robb had been stretchered from the field, we trouped off to the twice-weekly briefing given by the Prime Minister's press secretary – 'Government sources', to give him his official title. These off-the-record shindigs take place in extreme secrecy in a little turret room accessible by a spiral staircase. The effort of attendance is usually too onerous for a man of my constitution, so I send along a mate with a tape-recorder stuffed down his trousers, but today a personal appearance was called for. The purpose of the briefings is to disseminate the Prime Minister's ruminations by proxy; and if he hadn't been ruminating about Calder and Robb, he'd forgotten how to ruminate.

'Was the Prime Minister upset at the way the House

reacted to the announcement about the rail consortium?' I asked smoothly.

'He was disappointed,' came the reply.

'You mean hopping mad?'

'I mean disappointed. Why do you buggers have to make a song and dance of everything?' The press secretary's belligerence under fire was legendary.

'How did he think Robb handled the situation?' asked someone else.

'He thought he put the Government's case very' – a fractional pause – 'skilfully.'

'In other words, he cocked the whole thing up?'

Another fractional pause. 'That wasn't what I said.'

'Let's get this straight,' I said. 'My readers expect to hear things in plain English. You're saying Robb made a dog's dinner of it and the PM's given him a bollocking. Is that right?'

'That wasn't what I said,' he repeated. 'Matthew Robb has the full confidence of the Prime Minister who, as I say, thought he put the Government's case very – skilfully.'

Every journalist in the room was now scribbling furiously. Nothing sensational had been said and our wilder interpretations had been brushed aside. But there had still been those fractional pauses and that word of praise which hadn't sounded quite the way praise should. It was English hypocrisy at its best.

'So Robb's not likely to get Calder's job next week?' asked Bob Mumford.

'That's entirely a matter for the Prime Minister.'

'You wouldn't care to speculate?'

'I never speculate.'

'But we should still expect a reshuffle next week?'

'You can expect what you bloody well like,' said the press secretary gloomily. He hesitated. There was a silence you could cut with a knife. 'But I wouldn't get your knickers in a twist about it. Not like *some* papers,' he added, scowling at me.

My heart danced. It was all the corroboration I needed.

*

My piece the next morning merited three column inches and made the bottom of page two. I hadn't had such exposure since my famous dispatch from the shrubbery at Buckingham Palace, A RIGHT ROYAL BLOOMER.

CALDER TO STAY, ran my latest exclusive. Page two is the literary showcase of the paper, so the style was Jane Austen with a touch of Marcel Proust.

Transport Secretary Bernard Calder will NOT be given the sack next week.

His domestic crisis has BLOWN OVER and he is in GOOD HEALTH.

And his deputy Matthew Robb will NOT succeed him.

Robb made such a HASH of a statement in the Commons yesterday that one MP commented: 'It was DAYLIGHT ROBB-ERY.'

Later in the day, a rather nervous Bernard Calder sidled up to me in the Members Lobby.

'Aren't you jumping the gun, Beef? The PM hasn't actually said anything yet.'

'Put your faith in the popular press, my friend. There's no way he can promote Robb after yesterday's shambles. It was one of the most spectacular own-goals it's been my privilege to witness. You're safe as houses.'

'I still don't understand why there was such a fuss. The rail consortium's a sensational deal from the British point of view and the catering's just a side-show. People must realise that.'

'Of course they do. But it just needs Jack Bull to sound the battle-cry and they see things differently. Give the House a bit of patriotism on top of a good lunch and, if you've got an inexperienced, too-clever-by-half Minister at the dispatch-box, anything can happen.' I winked. 'How are your domestic affairs by the way?'

He winked back. 'It's funny you should ask, Beef. I was hopping mad when you printed that rubbish about my domestic crisis, but it's worked out wonderfully. Heather laughed her head off and everyone else has been rallying round as if I've suffered a family bereavement. When they thought I was happy at home, they were really snide about it: as soon as they reckoned I was knee-deep in the brown stuff, they started giving me sympathetic pats on the back and buying me drinks. I can't make it out.'

'That's politics, Bernard. Everyone loves a loser: it's one of the oldest rules of the House. They'll start rallying round Robb now.'

'That smarmy little shit? You're not serious.'

'Watch this space, Bernard. I'm writing a third article for tomorrow, in which Robb has the domestic crisis, you're the villain of the piece and the French are ratting on the deal. RESHUFFLE III. It should run and run.'

His jaw sagged until he realised I was kidding.

'You crafty bugger, Beef. You treat us like toys, don't you? Anything to sell a newspaper. We're just your tools.'

'You said it, Bernard. I'm off to Annie's. Time for a quick one?'

'Why not?'

'A bottle a day keeps the doctor away.'

'I'll drink to that.'

'Shall we take the lift?'

He nodded bravely, but his face was white as a sheet as I pressed the button for the ground floor.

9

BABY IN TREE SCANDAL

The House of Lords, as a general rule, is somewhere I avoid. I've nothing against chewing the rag with pensioners and the furniture and fittings can't be faulted. But socially the place is a nightmare. You get introduced to an old trout called Dalrymple of Inverkilduggan, the name doesn't register at all, then you realise it's because, as a younger trout down the other end of the building, you knew him as plain John Brown from the Gorbals. These things confuse the busy journalist.

An emergency, on the other hand, is an emergency. There's a barman in the House of Lords who mixes a bloody Mary which is like no bloody Mary I know. I don't know what he puts in it, but it has the kick of twenty mules and renews the lining of the solar plexus before you can say bottoms up. On that melancholy day last summer, when I put my shirt on a horse at Goodwood which developed gangrene of the fetlock a furlong from home, one of Eddy's specials was the order of the day.

The bar was deserted apart from a middle-aged woman sitting on her own in the corner. I studied her from stern to bow, as one does. She was smartly dressed and had once been beautiful: her hair had a strong natural wave and there was something firm and graceful in the lines of her mouth. She looked up, saw a large lobby correspondent blocking out the light and pulled a face. Then we recognised each other.

'John!'

'Susan!'

'What are you doing here?'

'I could ask the same of you. Come and join me.'

She came across and kissed me lightly on the cheek. A few pleasantries about my weight and the fact that none of us were getting any younger and we were back where we had started twenty-five years before. I said easily and naturally what I should have said then.

'I'm sorry, Susan.'

'Don't mention it.'

'That was a terrible thing I did. Journalism at its worst. I made your life hell.'

She gave a strange smile – of mischief, of regret, of absolution.

'We were young.'

My God, we were young. She can't have been more than twenty-five, but the real revelation was me. It was the year before I did my big spurt and, by sheer hard work and will-power, put on two stone in a month. My figure was going, you could say, but had not yet gone. I could walk half a mile without resting. I still bought off-the-peg suits. My thighs were like matchsticks. Nobody fainted when I walked into the room. Happy days.

My working life at that time was far more varied. Nowadays if you say you work for a tabloid, people reach for the deodorant: there wasn't the same stigma then. Instead of employing a single lobby correspondent to prop up the bar, my paper ran a team of four and we worked like beavers, getting every angle we could on every story. Dawn to dusk you could have seen me trotting round the Commons button-holing every Member I could. I barely knew where the bar was.

The pay was as rotten then as now, so I moonlighted as a racing tipster, football reporter and occasionally, if I was

lucky, restaurant critic. It was this interest in good food –
which I naïvely took to be the hallmark of a civilised man
and whose consequences I hadn't foreseen – which led to
my involvement with Susan. I was the subject of a certain
amount of teasing in the office and it was with mischievous
intent that my editor dispatched me to darkest Gloucestershire to interview a woman who had gone on hunger strike.

It was a shrewd move. A lot of newspaper interviews are
dull because the interviewer is bored stiff with the assignment; but if you can get the sparks to fly between interviewer and interviewee, lively copy is guaranteed. And
flying sparks could be anticipated here. As I mulled over
the position on the drive down, it was obvious the woman
I had to interview was a Grade I listed lunatic. Being an
energetic young Turk with strong views about what mattered in life, I intended to submit her to some tough questioning and expose her for the head-banger she undoubtedly
was.

Consider the facts. To go on hunger strike at the best of
times is a rash deed. You start going through bodily tor-
ments within hours, but it's days before the person you're
trying to blackmail has to lift a finger – there's no contest.
But to go on hunger strike over a field suggests the mental
processes of a retarded caterpillar.

Yes, a field. Piecing the story together from local news
reports, the woman in the case was a farmer's wife who was
upset because a motorway was scheduled to be built across
a corner of her land. She had been offered £1,000 for the
field, which would have fetched about three and sixpence
on the open market, but was having none of it. She had
insisted that the route of the motorway be moved two miles
to the west and wasn't touching any food till it was. Like I
said, pure fruitcake.

But you know how it is with women. Whether they act
rationally or irrationally pales into insignificance beside
their other qualities. The most sensible woman I've ever
met was a monster who ate barbed wire for breakfast. The
most perverse and muddle-headed was an absolute charmer

I would have put down my drink to kiss. Susan Hopwood was of the second type. The moment I set eyes on her – pale and drawn from her fast, but still beautiful in a rural English way – I was captivated.

'What can I do for you?' she asked, as I stood expectantly on the doorstep.

'I'd like to ask you a few questions. I'm a journalist.' In those days one said this with pride and it went over big. After Bobby Charlton and the Beatles and the Great Train Robbers, we were probably the most glamorous people in the country.

'Pleased to meet you. I'm sorry, I don't know your name.'

'Wellington. John Wellington.'

'Come inside, John.'

She showed me into the drawing-room and we sat down by the window. The house was one of those large, rambling affairs with clutter everywhere, but you couldn't call it cosy. The lingering smell of food, which you don't normally notice but is so intrinsic to the well-being of a normal household, was conspicuous by its absence.

I don't believe in pussy-footing my way through interviews, so I came straight out with it.

'What possesses a nice girl like you to go on hunger strike over a piece of grass? I've never heard of such a thing.'

She looked startled by my belligerence, but disarmed me with a smile.

'You are sweet. Have you come to talk me out of it?'

'Of course not. I'm a journalist, I don't take sides. If you want to do without your meat and two veg, that's your business. Kick the bucket in the process and we'll sell a few newspapers. I'm just trying to get to the bottom of these shenanigans. What's so special about a field?'

She pointed out of the window.

'It's that one at the end.'

'The one with the tree?'

'Yes.' The fruitcake motif returned and she gave me a dreamy look. 'That tree's been there nine hundred years. It was planted before the Battle of Hastings.'

'Nine hundred, you say?'

'It's the oldest tree in Gloucestershire. They call it the Great Oak of Cale. There's a morris dance there every Mayday. People come from miles around.'

I jotted all this down, adding by way of footnote: 'Not mad about grass. Mad about wood. Get picture of morris dancers.' I gave a thirsty pant, hoping she would offer me a glass of something, but no joy. These hunger-strikers just don't live in the real world. I soldiered on.

'So what you're basically saying is why chop something like that down to build a motorway? Why not re-route the motorway and keep everyone happy? Morris dancers, motorists, your good self, everyone.'

'Exactly.'

'Sounds sensible. What's the problem?'

'The problem,' she said, with bitter emphasis, 'is that all the land to the west of the tree is owned by Lord Cantlay.'

'Ah.'

'He's fighting any alternative route for the motorway tooth and nail. The Ministry of Transport won't say boo to him.'

I nodded gravely. You've probably heard of this Lord Cantlay. A prat through and through and one of the greatest living Englishmen. Landowner extraordinary, press baron, round-the-world yachtsman, you name it. When men like Lord Cantlay say 'No can do', you don't argue: you touch your forelock and say 'Yes, my Lord.'

I put down my notebook. 'These are dark waters, Susan, but I'm beginning to see a glimmer of light. Little Woman versus Big Man. It's good copy. Add the tree, the Battle of Hastings and assorted morris dancers and you have the makings of a story. The trouble is, it's not really page one stuff – not until you've lost another four stone, that is, and we want to avoid that. I'd like to help you, Susan, but it's difficult. I'm sorry.'

She looked at me appealingly and my heart went out to her. I used to think that, for sheer sex appeal, there was nothing to beat a woman who'd just finished a four-course meal and had that full, contented look. The salad-eating members of the sex leave me cold. But there was something so pitiable about this girl, with her white cheeks and her sunken eyes and her clothes that were far too big for her, that I was quite overcome. My voice cracked with emotion and, on an absurd impulse, I reached across and took her hand in mine.

'Trust me, Susan. I think you're daft as a brush and, if I'd ever turned away food on this scale, my mother would have given me a good thrashing. But if it's you against Cantlay, I want you to win. You know the phrase "campaigning journalism"? Well, you're about to see campaigning journalism of no common order. I'll go straight to the Minister of Transport tomorrow and give him an earful. I'll get the whole of Fleet Street on your side. I'll do things you didn't think were possible in this lax post-war world. But first,' I said, rising to my feet, 'we're going to have lunch.'

'Are you joking?'

'You don't have to have any. You can watch me and get the pleasure vicariously, if that's the word I'm looking for. There's a place in the *Good Food Guide* just up the road and I want to check it out. Are you coming?'

We got in my car and drove off: past the field, past the Great Oak, past a flock of sheep, past the village church, past the post office, past a little country pub with a thatched roof and honeysuckle on the wall and a bowered garden meandering down to the river. And a great peace set in. We didn't say very much, but there was a good feeling between us, a very good feeling. I could have stayed with her all day and all the next day and not wanted to be anywhere else. London seemed a long way off.

Lunch could have been a strain – self falling on the food like a tiger, Susan cold-shouldering it, waiters exchanging glances – but it wasn't. We talked about everything under the sun: from politics to films, from Czechoslovakia to cricket, from the Pope to Scottish railway timetables. Get her off the subject of trees and she had so much charm it hurt: there was a verve about her, and a grace, and a playfulness in the eyes, and a sweetness, which move me still.

It was at that lunch, quite unexpectedly, that she first mentioned Johnny Hall.

'You really know Johnny?' I said, impressed.

'I only met him once. At a party.'

'What's he like?'

'Devastating.'

'Everything he's cracked up to be?'

'Definitely.'

The name may not mean much now, but in the swinging Sixties there was nobody, nobody, who swung like Johnny. He was a pop star of sorts, but it wasn't his voice which made him a legend, but his testosterone. If he was giving a concert in Manchester, mothers in Birmingham locked up their daughters for the night. He went through British society like a dose of salts. He was insatiable. During one famous gig in Leamington Spa, his conquests were rumoured to run into double figures before midnight struck.

The press, of course, loved him. At the peak of his activity we had four full-time staff chasing up Johnny Hall stories, with reinforcements on stand-by on the sports page and foreign news desk. The tabloids had been in the doldrums, mere pocket versions of our illustrious rivals: singlehandedly almost, he raised us to our present levels.

It was his sheer newsworthiness which put an idea into my head. 'Had you thought of using Johnny?' I asked Susan, finishing off the *selle d'agneau aux fines herbes* with a flourish.

'How do you mean?'

'If he came out on the side of the oak, that *would* be front-page news.'

'But I only met him once.'

'How long ago?'

'Last month. There were a lot of other people. He won't remember me.'

'Worth a try, don't you think?'

'I shouldn't think so.'

We left it at that. I had a couple of *tartes aux cerises* and a slab of stilton and drove her home, where her husband had finished on the farm and was waiting for us. A stolid, earnest type with a lethal line in small-talk about foot-and-mouth disease: probably, at that tender stage of my life, the most boring man I'd ever come across. Seeing the two of them together sent a great wave of sadness through me. It's always the way with beautiful women: they throw themselves away on 100−1 shots and leave the rest of us wailing and gnashing our teeth in the outer darkness. But what a waste.

I took one last look at the oak and, with very mixed feelings, drove back to London.

It seems odd to me now, when I'm on Christian name terms with the highest in the land, but in those days lobby correspondents approached Ministers in an attitude of deference. The Minister of Transport was a peppery, rather aloof man called Leighton and there was no question of slapping him on the back and saying 'What about this motorway, old cock?' One had to grovel.

I lay in wait for him after the ten o'clock vote and made my approach as he was leaving the Chamber through the Members Lobby.

'Excuse me. Mr Leighton?'

'Yes, yes, what is it?'

I wasn't so physically distinctive then and I don't think he knew who I was.

'Can I have a very quick word?'

'Yes, yes, go ahead.'

'It's about this woman on hunger strike over the motorway.'

'The one in Gloucestershire?'

'That's her. Susan Hopwood.'

'Yes, yes, yes. I know who you mean.'

'I did an interview with her yesterday. I think she means business.'

'She does, does she?'

174

'I think so. She's extremely determined. There's a nine-hundred-year-old oak which is going to have to be cut down and she's very upset about it. Is it worth the Government having a corpse on its hands just for the sake of a motorway?'

He considered this point for about a second and a half. I wouldn't describe him as a man in whom the milk of human kindness flowed by the pailful.

'What's one silly woman more or less? We've been through the proper appeal procedures. There's nothing to be done.'

'She's a rather *nice* silly woman.'

'Bugger that. We're not running a charity. Why not try and bring her to her senses instead of bothering me?'

He strode off, leaving me feeling pretty disconsolate. If this sort of thing happened today, I'd know what to do. Every politician I've ever met is open to some form of blackmail: you just need to dig up the right bit of dirt and you can bend them to your will. What I should have done was concentrate on the London end and try to bring pressure to bear on Leighton. But I was too young, too inexperienced. I reached for the blunderbuss when I should have used a rapier. I achieved my goal – but at a cost.

ANGUISH OF JOHNNY'S GIRL, ran the front-page headline in next morning's paper. I sweated long into the night over the article and, though I say it myself, the prose fairly fizzed. Without saying anything actionable, I left the casual reader in no doubt that the woman doing without her vitamins to save the tree was the same woman who had been seen talking to Johnny Hall at a party the previous month. What's more, they were 'friends'. This may not sound like hot stuff, but you must remember that the Sixties were the Golden Age of English euphemism: calling people friends was dynamite. Knowing Johnny's track-record, I was confident the story would run and run.

It's always good to see your name in lights on the front

page and I was savouring the nuances of my prose over breakfast, as journalists do, when the telephone rang. It was Susan.

'What the hell do you think you're playing at?'

I was dumbfounded. Ingratitude, thou marble-hearted fiend, was the general drift of my thoughts.

'Trying to save your bacon, of course. You need publicity, I've got you publicity. I drew a blank with the Minister, so I put plan B into action. What's wrong?'

'What's wrong is that there are twenty journalists camped outside the house.'

'Isn't that what you wanted?'

'They're not interested in the tree, they're interested in me and Johnny.'

'What of it? Play a straight bat about Johnny and bring the subject round to the tree at every opportunity. Had you thought of holding a press conference standing next to it? The photos would be sensational.'

There was a short pause and I could hear her breathing heavily down the line.

'John, I'm a married woman.'

'Yes?'

'Do I have to spell it out? Being "Johnnny's girl" is *not* the sort of publicity a woman wants when she's married to someone else. Well, is it?'

I weighed this. Women were as much a closed book to me then as now, but she had what you might call a good debating point. Not one to fight dirty in an argument, I conceded that her being married might, to some people, have a bearing on the situation.

'You bet it might. You should have thought of that before barging into my affairs. Listen,' she went on, softening. 'Is there any chance you could come down?'

'I'd be delighted.'

'There's been a new development and all these reporters are giving me the jitters.'

'Quite understood. I'll be with you by two thirty.'

*

Not many people had car radios in those days, so I had to stop off in the Dog and Duck in Swindon to catch the lunchtime news on television. Things couldn't have been going better. The story was second item and a harassed-looking Leighton was shown being interviewed outside the Ministry of Transport. 'If the woman has a genuine grievance,' he snapped, 'I shall look into the matter again.' A U-turn looked imminent.

I had a few jars and motored down to Gloucestershire. Susan hadn't exaggerated about the waiting press hordes. There must have been thirty reporters in the drive and photographers had scrambled up trees to get a better view. In these more hectic days, it would take a toothache at Balmoral to draw that sort of crowd.

I greeted some of my partners in crime, then passed confidently through the throng. To shouts of 'Scab!' from the wits at the back, I rang the bell and was admitted.

Imagine how I felt when I found Susan in the kitchen tucking into a large plate of eggs, sausages, bacon, tomatoes, mushrooms, black pudding and, if my eyes didn't deceive me, jacket potatoes with lashings of butter. A magnificent sight, of course, from a purely aesthetic viewpoint, but in all the circumstances a bit rich. I mean, there was I leaving no stone unturned to ensure that her sacrifices were rewarded, and she rats on her side of the bargain. Two more days looking wan and emaciated and she would have had Leighton by the short and curlies. But you can't look wan and emaciated on that sort of diet. I know. I've tried it.

I helped myself to some black pudding and a couple of bangers and reproved her sternly.

'There's only one word to describe this performance, Susan, and it's backsliding. I admit my Johnny Hall idea brought sorrow as well as joy, but its heart was in the right place. The oak will stand, the motorway will be diverted and you will live to tell the tale – I call that quite a hat-trick. But it only takes one of those reporters to stick his head through the window and see this little orgy and all bets are off. JOHNNY'S GIRL NEEDS HER RATIONS. HYPOCRISY OF THE

TREE WOMAN. I can see it coming a mile off. Woman, thy name is frailty,' I added, remembering a good one from Tennyson.

She smiled and it was one of the most winning smiles I'd ever seen. Mischievous, mysterious, almost tender. I could never keep up with Susan, but it didn't seem to matter: she had a great gift for friendship and for keeping the peace.

'I'm sorry, John. There's been a new development. I'm under doctor's orders.'

'What have doctors got to do with it?'

'I'm eating for two.'

'You don't mean –?'

'I'm pregnant.'

I nearly choked on my sausage. In these reckless days you hardly meet a woman of child-bearing age who doesn't give it a whirl at least once. The phrase 'I'm pregnant' is practically a colloquialism: there are whole afternoons in the Strangers cafeteria when you hear nothing else. But this was the selfish Sixties. Marriage was on the way out. The Abortion Act had just been passed. The Pill was available over the counter at every self-respecting off-licence. Women of Susan's type simply didn't get pregnant – or, if they did, they didn't announce the fact to passing journalists. I was stunned.

'Congratulations,' I muttered, resuming the sausage with difficulty. 'This certainly puts a new complexion on things. When did you find out?'

'This morning. The doctor said I had to get back on my food at once. He said I was lucky I hadn't lost the child already. And then there's my husband. He's insisting I look after myself properly.'

'You realise you're taking all the pressure off Leighton?'

'Of course. But what can I do?'

I pondered. What could she do? I had a lot of respect for my fellow hacks in those days and I couldn't see them having the wool pulled over their eyes for much longer. A woman starving to death and a woman wolfing half the contents of her fridge are not the same animal. These things

178

have a way of manifesting themselves. I'm a living monument to that.

'We must act quickly,' I said. 'It's a gamble, but I think it will work. Barricade yourself in here for a few days and admit no visitors. If you have to eat — and I'm the last person to object on ideological grounds — close the curtains first. Some of these new-look photographers have things called telephoto lenses. They're lethal: they'll change the face of British journalism, mark my words. But we'll have to feed that rabble some sort of story or they'll storm the house. You can't talk to them yourself because you smell of sausages, and I don't trust your husband. Expectant fathers are notoriously given to boasting. I'll have to deal with them myself.'

Her eyes lit up in gratitude. 'John, would you really?'

'It will be a pleasure. I owe it to you. Just finish that egg and make yourself scarce.'

She did so, pausing to remark that there was nothing to beat good food. I concurred and added that she would have saved everyone a lot of trouble if she'd remembered that two weeks ago. She said principles were principles and you had to take a stand sometimes. I asked her what principles were. She called me a heathen. I called her a lunatic. Like I say, one lovely woman.

I took a deep breath and stepped out to confront the waiting press corps. Someone at the back called out, 'It's only Beef' and someone else lobbed an orange which passed over my left shoulder, but the others greeted me respectfully. Working in Fleet Street then gave you a certain cachet and, as the name of my paper passed from lip to lip, there was a deferential hush. 'What news, sir?' asked a little man from the *Cheltenham Echo*, and I can hear that 'sir' still.

'Mrs Hopwood is too ill to meet the press,' I announced gravely. 'She sends her apologies and has asked me to answer any questions you gentlemen may have.'

'Did she say anything about Johnny Hall?'

'Not a word.'

'No special messages? No plans to see him?'

'Nothing.'

There were groans of disappointment and the reporters at the back started to pack their bags.

'She must have said *something*,' came a persistent voice.

'She did. But not about Johnny. She's very worried about the tree.'

'The tree?'

'That's right. The tree. She talked at length about it.'

This was greeted with disbelief, not to say ridicule. Hack turned to hack and said, 'Did the man say tree?' Scepticism lay like a scar on those hard-bitten faces. I knew how they felt. If you've been camped outside somebody's house all day, you expect something pretty salty from the man who's got the inside gen: when all he talks about is trees, you're entitled to your little grumble. Still, as I was engaged for the defence, so to speak, I felt obliged to do my bit.

'The Greak Oak of Cale,' I said, pointing theatrically. 'Planted nine hundred years ago in the reign of King Harold. A landmark for miles around. The scene of morris dancing every May. Much loved by local villagers. Now to be cut down to make a motorway because Lord Cantlay won't give up any of his land. That, gentlemen, is why Susan Hopwood is starving herself to death.'

I gave it my best shot, but the material was pretty thin whichever way you looked at it. You've got to remember that nobody gave a bugger about the environment in those days: a tree was a block of wood and that was that. The trickle to the exit became a stampede and there were only a handful of diehards left by the time I'd finished. One of them was a small ferret-faced man I'd come across once before, on an assignment in Birmingham. Irwin, he was called.

'Do you really think Mrs Hopwood will starve herself to death?' he asked, looking at me intently.

I side-stepped the question. 'If she has nothing more to eat, she will die.'

'How soon?' asked a lugubrious man in black, keen to get home to his dinner.

'I couldn't say. I'm not an expert. She's very thin already.'

'How thin's thin?'

'I'm not an expert on that either.'

'Has she seen a doctor?' asked Irwin.

'She saw her doctor this morning.'

'What did he have to say about her condition?'

'Obviously he was very concerned about it.'

'What's his name?' Irwin asked, pencil poised. Too late I saw the danger.

'I don't know. Not relevant, surely?'

'It might be,' he muttered. 'It just might be.'

Two hours later I saw him in a call-box in the village with his notebook at the ready and a smug look on his face. I know those smug looks. They're peculiar to people who've just had sex and journalists on the verge of a scoop. As no woman in Gloucestershire would have touched Irwin with a barge-pole, I feared the worst.

JOHNNY'S LOVE CHILD was the headline they gave it and I have to say it was a very professional job. Irwin had tracked down the doctor, got the low-down and written it up with gusto. He got the identity of the father wrong, of course, but what's a detail like that in the great sweep of history?

If there had been difficulties up to now persuading the press to ignore the Johnny angle and give their attention to the tree, they were mightily compounded by this new development.

Johnny himself was unavailable for comment, being engaged on one of those pilgrimages to the Himalayas which pop stars of the time favoured, but the media siege of the Hopwood residence resumed with a vengeance. Susan issued a statement confirming that she was pregnant and had abandoned her hunger strike; she also threatened to sue Irwin's paper. And a gleeful Minister of Transport appeared on the nine o'clock news to announce that the motorway would proceed as planned. 'I think

Mrs Hopwood's case has lost some of its credibility,' he said with a ghastly smirk.

A very angry Susan was on the telephone to me two days later. 'I hope I never see another journalist in my life. What a miserable, twisted lot of bastards you are. I suppose you're too arrogant to admit that this is your fault?'

I wasn't having this. 'Who went on hunger strike? Who got worked up over a tree?'

'That's nothing to do with it.'

'It's everything to do with it. Anyone who mounts a big publicity campaign like that is putting themselves in the firing line. She who lives by the media dies by the media,' I added, a radical sentiment for the Sixties.

'You just won't admit you're wrong, will you? I didn't ask you to bring Johnny into it, but you blundered on and turned the whole thing into a nightmare. Anyone with any normal feelings would apologise, but I'm wasting my breath with you. Perhaps you'll be interested to know that James is never talking to me again.'

'James?'

'My husband.'

'Oh, yes. Him.'

I thought about this. Having met the man and found him, as I think I mentioned, one of the most lethal bores who ever wore green wellies and grumbled about the Common Market, this didn't sound like a great loss. But I saw practical difficulties.

'Won't that make living together rather awkward? Suppose, for example, James wanted to take the Land-Rover to a point-to-point when you were planning a big shop at Sainsbury's? Or imagine –'

'He's divorcing me, you fool.'

'Ah.'

'I thought you'd like to know.'

'Yes, quite.'

'Seeing that it's all your fault.'

'Absolutely.'

This did shake me. I was about to mumble my apologies

when she put the receiver down; and as it's no good mumbling your apologies into thin air, I never got around to it. A piece in the papers a few months later confirmed that she had got divorced and a few months after that the birth of a baby girl was announced. Felicity Jane, if I remember correctly. On the same day there was a picture of lumberjacks chopping down the Great Oak of Cale while a troupe of morris dancers wept hot tears in the background . . .

'What I still find so extraordinary,' I pronounced, a quarter of a century on, closeted in a bar in the House of Lords with this wonderful, exasperating woman, 'is the sheer speed with which everything happened. Nowadays it's what you'd expect. Modern communications are faster and newspapers live from hand to mouth. We chew people up and spit them out in a matter of hours. But those were more leisurely times. If I'd had any idea how quickly the whole thing would blow up in our faces, I'd never have brought Johnny into the picture.' I threw her a shy smile. 'You do know that, don't you, Susan?'

'Of course.'

'I was on your side. I wanted you to win.'

'Of course you did.'

'I just made one of those almighty cock-ups to which the working journalist is prone. It's the story of my life,' I added, looking at my bloody Mary, my half-finished cigarette, my dog-eared tie, my stomach sloping away towards the horizon.

She hesitated. 'John, there's something you should know. Can you keep a secret?'

'Not normally. I'm prepared to make an exception.'

'I'll trust you.' Again she hesitated. 'I just thought it was an irony you'd appreciate. Johnny was the father.'

'Come again?'

'Johnny Hall. He was the father of my child.'

I stared at her. 'But you said you only met him once.'

'Oh, for Heaven's sake!' She threw back her head and let out a great peal of laughter. 'I did only meet him once. It only takes five minutes to make a baby – two if you're Johnny Hall. It was the Sixties.'

'That's true.'

'Everyone was doing it.'

'So they were.'

'I had more one-night stands than I had hot dinners.'

'I'm sure you did.'

I puffed sadly at my cigarette. I'd heard it went on, but I'd never really believed it happened to people I knew, if you see what I mean. I'd been too busy putting on weight to notice these great social upheavals.

Another thought struck me. 'If Johnny was the father, it's you who owe me an apology. Fancy giving me a bollocking for reporting the facts accurately for once in my life! A bit rich, Susan.'

'I know. I'm sorry.'

'Make nothing of it.'

'I was rather fraught. It was a bad time in my life.'

'Water under the bridge. I deserved everything I got. Another drink?'

'Yes, please.'

We paused and waited for reinforcements to arrive. Susan smiled and I smiled back. I don't think I've ever met a woman with whom I felt so at ease, so supremely, deliciously comfortable.

'Tell me about your daughter,' I said. 'If she's Johnny's girl, she must be quite a cracker. How old is she now? Twenty-five?'

'Twenty-four.'

'In one of the more flamboyant professions, I imagine. A rock singer if I know Johnny's hormones. I picture her doing gigs in smoky night-clubs in Amsterdam. Tramping round Europe half stoned with a rucksack on her back.'

'She's a stockbroker.'

'You're not serious.'

'With an American merchant bank.' She gave a wan smile. 'Fleet Street isn't the only thing that's changed. Do you want to know what she's earning?'

I held up my hands in horror. 'Don't rub it in. I'm not a vindictive man, but I do have to earn my crust as a journalist and the wounds are still fresh. Let's just take it she's doing nicely.'

'All right.'

'And you're doing nicely too, Susan. As lovely as you ever were, if you don't mind a clapped-out old hack saying so. Leaving aside the fact that you're an oak short, a husband short and that superannuated prat Lord Cantlay stuffed you over the motorway, I'd say you were sitting pretty. Very pretty.'

I stopped. I'd suddenly noticed the wedding ring on her finger.

'You've remarried?'

'Yes.' She started to laugh. It was just a giggle at first, then it swelled and swelled until her whole body was convulsed. 'A marriage of convenience!'

'What do you mean?'

'Wake up, John. I'm not going to let a man like Lord Cantlay have the last laugh, am I? Our poor farm was decimated by the motorway and his fifty thousand acres were untouched.'

'So?'

She carried on laughing: there was no stopping her. When she finally weakened, she held out a limp hand for me to shake.

'John, meet the wife of the thirteenth Earl of Cantlay.'

I stammered my congratulations, but had the same thought I'd had twenty-five years before, when I met her dolt of a first husband. What a waste! What a terrible bloody waste!

IO

WE WUZ ROBBED!

'Can I have a word please, Roger?'
  'I'm sorry, Beef, I'm rather pushed.'
  'A very quick one.'
  'I really can't stop.'
  'It won't take a minute.'
  'Not now, Beef.'
  'Perhaps over a large brandy –'
  'Another time.'
I wonder if you notice anything about the above dialogue?
No? You don't have my nose for hidden meanings. You
haven't plied a dirty trade for as many years as I have. It
struck me straight away.

The first speaker in the scene (myself, well oiled after a
good lunch) is all charm and courtesy and sweet reasonableness. The second (Rt Hon Roger Abrahams, last Chancellor
of the Exchequer but three) is a shade brusque. Study his
words carefully and you'll see that his heart isn't in the
conversation. He's distracted. His mind strays from the
point. He wants to be somewhere else. He doesn't – and
this is the point which may have escaped you – want to
spend the afternoon putting the world to rights with overweight lobby correspondents.

Which was all very peculiar.

Roger Abrahams is one of the great men of the House
of Commons. Ex-Chancellor of the Exchequer, ex-Health

Secretary, ex-Lord Privy Seal, ex-practically everything. And the marvellous thing is, none of it's gone to his head. He's as plain and straightforward and affable as the day he first came to the House. No side, no condescension, no elder statesman airs, nothing. A lovely man and, more to the point, a very approachable man. Practically his greatest pleasure in life, now he's retired to the backbenches, is to chat to old muckers like me with a glass of something good in his hand and his favourite pipe sticking out of his mouth.

So why the startled rabbit impersonations? I was stumped. There was a shifty, furtive, *hunted* look in his eyes I'd never seen before. I smelled a rat. I smelled several rats. A large rodent colony had sprung up before my eyes in the Mother of Parliaments.

There was nothing to be done for the moment, so I bided my time and waited till we were alone together in Annie's the following day. It was one of those flat, grey Tuesday afternoons when strong men sag and the hooch sticks in the throat and life barely seems worth crossing the road to say hullo to. Roger had lost his hunted look, but there was still something sad and rather downtrodden about him. The jolly Roger of popular repute was just a memory.

'Do you believe in Fate, Beef?' he asked suddenly, puffing at his pipe and staring out of the window.

It was a big question for a Tuesday. Abstract. Philosophical. Religious almost. Not this speaker's usual style at all.

'I'm not sure,' I replied, slipping into the same idiom. 'I once put a tenner on a horse at Wincanton because it had a Y in its name and I'd passed a Y-shaped tree on the way to the course. It romped home at 100–30. On another, less happy occasion –'

'Not that sort of Fate, you clown.' He took another puff at his pipe. 'I'm talking about something far more sinister. I'm talking about the Fate which follows you all your life and catches up with you just when you think you've escaped it. Retribution.'

I began to get his drift. 'Like not paying your TV licence, then your set packs up in the middle of the Cup Final?'

'More or less. I've been thinking about retribution a lot lately, Beef. And the way Fate catches up with you. Another drink?'

'Isn't it my shout?'

'No, I'm in the chair.'

'Are you sure?'

'Positive.'

I'll say this for Roger. He may have been the worst Chancellor since the war, but he's got a bloody good head for figures. I'd bought him a drink, he'd bought me one, Tiger had got the third round, we'd both got Tiger one, Ginger had popped in with a bottle of champers, I'd got a bloody Mary for George, then we'd settled down for some serious drinking. It's easy to lose track of these things. I could have sworn it was my turn and would have stumped up like a gentleman. The paper was paying. But if Roger said he was in the chair, he was in the chair. No arguing.

He took a dog-eared piece of paper out of his pocket and passed it to me. 'Have you seen this?'

'It's a copy of your entry in *Who's Who*.'

'Read it.'

'Roger, please. Is this kind? Is this reasonable?'

'Read it.'

I skimmed through. '"Born, Manchester, 7 August 1920 ... Educated Manchester Grammar School, LSE ... Married Valerie, only daughter of the late Sam and May Ramsbotham ..." Roger, I don't mean to be personal, but this is yesterday's news. With all the will in the world, we couldn't make a story out of it. We've got shareholders to answer to. Perhaps a nice letter to the *Dictionary of National Biography* or some minor American university ...'

'Read the bit about recreations.'

'"Walking and reading."'

'Walking and –?'

'Reading.'

'Fate,' he said, crunching his pipe with his teeth. 'That's what it is. Fate.'

I think, if there had been a doctor in the bar, or even a

vet, I would by now have sought a professional opinion. Having served his country like a lion for thirty-five years, the Rt Hon Roger Abrahams was showing every sign of succumbing to senile dementia. It brought a lump to my throat to see that fine yeomanlike mind wandering like this: the kindest thing seemed to be to offer him the Chiltern Hundreds and put him in some kind of home. I was about to ask George to call a taxi when Roger dipped into his other pocket and produced exhibit B, a cutting from one of the posher Sundays. I studied it.

'"This year's Damascus Prize judges have been announced. The chairman will be the Rt Hon Roger . . ."' I saw a glimmer of light. 'Is this that big literary prize? The novels nobody wants to read by the writers nobody's heard of?'

'That's the one.'

'Good God.'

'Is He good? Not to me, He isn't.'

'Profound condolences and so on. I wouldn't touch that sort of gig if you paid me in gold ingots. Still, I suppose if you enjoy reading –'

'I *don't* enjoy reading!'

'But I thought –'

'My idea of a good read is the sports page of the *News of the World*. I can't stand novels. Novels are for women and men in corduroy trousers. The last novel I read was *Winnie the Pooh*. The whole thing's a disaster.'

'So why –?'

'Will you stop interrupting and *listen*!' He was practically purple with fury: I've never seen him so mad. 'You remember what I was saying about Fate? How it waits and waits and then grabs you by the short and curlies? All this started thirty years ago, when I was first elected. Thirty years, Beef! You know how *Who's Who* and *Dod's* and all the other periodicals flood new MPs with questionnaires about their backgrounds?'

'Of course.'

'Well, one of the questions was about recreations. Beef,

I didn't *have* any recreations. Recreations, my arse! In my part of Manchester, people didn't know what the word meant. We worked our arses off during the day, then we got ratted in the evening. Every now and again, one of us got completely paralytic and stood for Parliament. But we didn't go poncing off to the opera or joining golf clubs or doing evening classes in Italian or any of that crap. We had better things to do.'

'Like getting ratted?'

'Like getting ratted.'

'Spoken like an Englishman. Why didn't you just say so?'

'I did, Beef. That's the terrible thing. I can remember it as if it was yesterday. I was filling in one of these forms in the smoking room during an all-night sitting on the Finance Bill and I'd just got to the bit about recreations. I was using a blue fountain-pen and I wrote NONE in big letters for the whole world to see. I wasn't ashamed of it. Then Tim Clutton suddenly appeared over my left shoulder.'

'The Chief Whip with the squint?'

'That's the one. He was pairing Whip then. Biggest bastard I've ever met. Nice man. He saw what I'd written and said, "Are you sure that's sensible, Roger?" in an odd sort of voice. I asked what he meant and he said it looked bad if a Member didn't have any interests outside politics. I said I didn't have any interests – none that were printable – and he said, well, make something up, it will be good for your career.' He stopped and made a gesture of resignation with his pipe. 'I was a young man, Beef. I didn't know any better. It was the littlest, whitest lie a politician ever told. How could I possibly see that it would return to haunt me?'

I was deeply moved. I've seen tragedies unfold in my time, many of them in this very bar, but this one had a piquancy it was hard to parallel. If Fate was going to lie in wait for people who told whoppers and club them over the head thirty years later, the outlook for my profession was desperate.

'You can guess the rest,' he went on. 'The promoters of this prize wanted some well-known figure to chair the judges. They scoured *Who's Who* for some sucker they could nobble – and Abrahams was first out of the hat.'

I spotted the flaw in the plot. 'Why didn't you just tell them to get lost? You didn't have to do it.'

He writhed on his stool. 'You haven't been listening, have you, Beef? I said Fate had got me by the short and curlies and you thought I was exaggerating. How about this for a diabolical piece of luck? Two weeks ago, I took a parliamentary delegation to Hong Kong.'

'Nice spot, I'm told.'

'While I was away, I told my secretary to deal with the routine correspondence but leave anything substantial till I got back.'

'Eminently sensible arrangements.'

'I get begging letters the whole time asking me to be chairman of this or patron of that or honorary president of the other. I told Susan to draft replies for me to sign later unless – and this is the devilry of it – unless there was a fee involved. In that case she was to use her discretion and accept on my behalf if she thought it was suitable. I've been a bit short lately, Beef.'

'I'm so sorry. Big mortgage?'

'It's nothing serious, but the odd lump sum helps a bit.'

'I'm sure it does.'

'So she went and accepted the bloody thing. I'd back out tomorrow, but it would look bad. And, of course, if you believe in Fate, it serves me right. I've been punished for telling a lie and now I'm being punished for being greedy. The Damascus Foundation's so-called fee is barely enough to keep me in pipe-tobacco. It works out at about 37p per novel – assuming you read them, which I don't have the slightest intention of doing. As for mixing with all those arty-farty literary types . . .' He shuddered. 'I can't tell you how much I'm dreading this, Beef. I felt far less nervous before my first Budget, when I had to put 20p on a packet of cigarettes.'

I commiserated. 'The other moral, presumably, is not to go on junkets to Hong Kong?'

'It's not funny, Beef.'

'Of course it isn't. On the other hand,' I said quickly, 'you may be able to have the last laugh. Don't Ladbroke's run a book on the Damascus Prize? I seem to remember a Jamaican woman cantering home at 8–1 last year and wishing I'd had a few quid on her. The clouds are gathering, Roger, but there are blue skies to the west. Some good may finally come from these dark days in your life.'

'What are you chuntering on about?'

'Watch this space.'

I rather lost track of Roger for a few months after that. Once I spied him across the Members Lobby scuttling into the post office with a book in his hand. Another time I saw him trudging down Victoria Street, head bowed, brows knitted, like a man with the cares of the world on his shoulders. On the Saturday of the Lord's Test, he could be observed reading a book in the Warner stand. Reading a book – with Greenidge batting! But I had no idea of the purgatory he was going through until he burst into Annie's at ten fifteen on a Monday morning in July.

'Brandy, George!'

He knocked it back like a man helping down an aspirin and ordered another. Then he noticed the large figure blocking out the light at the other end of the bar.

'You're in early, aren't you, Beef?'

'I could say the same for you.'

I thought his point misconceived. London-based lobby correspondents often arrive at the office early if they're feeling thirsty, but northern MPs have further to come: on Mondays they turn up in dribs and drabs, with the Member for John o'Groats North-West bringing up the rear. But his mood interested me strangely. He looked like an elder statesman who had been dragged through a hedge by a team of oxen.

'You look,' I began, thinking this quite a passable one for a Monday morning, when the level of repartee isn't too hot, 'like an elder statesman who –'

He held up a warning hand. 'Beef, please. I'm not ready for it yet. I need sympathy. By the bucketful. I've just been through my most hair-raising ordeal since the Normandy landings. Would you say I was a fair man, Beef?'

'None fairer.'

'Would you say I was someone who kept his head while everyone about was losing theirs?'

'Something to that effect.'

'Would you say I was a man to hit a woman over the head with a bottle while diplomatic channels were still open?'

'Roger, you didn't.'

'No,' he conceded, gulping his brandy. 'I didn't. But I damn nearly did. It was nip and tuck. My hand gripped the bottle and I thought, If you use that word once more, Sabina, I'll brain you. Then she did use it. Twice. In one sentence. I picked up the bottle. I chose a spot just above her left ear. I steeled myself. Then I suddenly remembered I'd been Chancellor of the Exchequer for three years and that restrained me. It didn't fit the part somehow.'

'You can't put 40p on a bottle of spirits one minute, then use the bottle as a blackjack the next?'

'Exactly.'

'I think,' I said firmly, 'that if you want sympathy by the bucketful, you'll have to provide footnotes for your slower readers. Who is this woman Sabina? What is the word she uses which drives you up the wall? And, last but not least, how much drink was left in the bottle? A working journalist must know these things.'

'You're quite right, Beef. I'm sorry, I'm not myself. Sabina Umlaut, so you can avoid her, is what's called a literary critic.'

'Ah.'

'She's one of the other judges for this Damascus Prize. We've just spent the weekend in Hay-on-Wye drawing up the short list.' He pulled a face. 'Ye gods! If Cabinet meetings were like that . . .'

'Blood on the carpet?'

'Blood? Beef, you haven't lived, you just haven't lived.

Julian locked himself in his room for an hour. Quentin threw a glass of wine in Jasmin's face. There was mayhem.'

'Julian? Quentin? Jasmin? Weren't there any real people there?'

'The only halfway real person was the woman who brought the sandwiches, and she was called Myfanwy. I tell you, Beef, I felt like a goldfish among sharks. We politicians have our differences, but we play the game and we only take the gloves off in election years. If a woman like Sabina were ever elected to the House of Commons –'

A coronary of some kind seemed imminent, so I intervened. 'Calm yourself, Roger. Have another drink. The main thing is, did you actually agree a short list?'

'Only just.'

'Let's see it then.'

He took a piece of paper out of his wallet on which he'd scribbled the titles of the books. I ran a jaded eye over it.

'*Janus. Vale of Tears. Mandy's War. The Second Coming of Franz von Hauser* – that's rather a mouthful, I suppose it's a whodunnit. *A Fashionable Host.* Last but not least, *The Imbroglio.* What the hell's an imbroglio?'

'Don't ask me.'

'George?'

'Sorry, Beef.'

Tiger was deep in the crossword at the far end of the bar. I consulted the oracle.

'Imbroglio, Tiger. Ten letters. Any thoughts?'

'I think it means a cock-up.'

'Thank you, Tiger. Presumably the hero's an Italian journalist?'

'How should I know?' said Roger. 'I haven't read the damn thing.'

'So how did you –'

'I bluffed, Beef. I waffled. I bullshitted like there was no tomorrow. It was just like the good old days at the Treasury.' He put down his pipe and grinned. 'You don't learn much about life as one of Her Majesty's Ministers, Beef, but one thing you do learn is how to chair a meeting. You learn how to play A off against B and get C to agree with D and come to a decision just as everyone's getting thirsty. At the Chevening weekends when I was Chancellor, when we were drawing up the Budget, I used to sit there like Buddha for hours at a time, listening to the arguments, seeing who was on whose side, taking notes – and then I'd announce that a consensus had emerged and say what I thought it was.'

'That's how you did it. I thought you stuck pins in a bit of paper.'

He ignored the crack. Often the best way with cracks.

'I tried the same thing at Hay-on-Wye with this mob. Ye gods, it took a long time to work. We arrived. We introduced ourselves. The others had all been sleeping with each other since Cambridge, so that didn't take long. We sat down. We had a bottle of wine and some sandwiches. We got to work. I proposed that the other four write down their first six choices in order of preference and I would then operate the single-transferable-vote system as used in German parliamentary elections.'

'Brilliant!'

'I thought so, Beef. Fair, simple, scientific. They've had stable government in Bonn since 1945. Did they listen? Not on your arse. Julian pulled a face and said we weren't in the House of Commons and Quentin – he's a publisher, they're the worst of the lot – said we should discuss the merits of all the books and do any voting at the end.' He drained his drink and ordered another. 'Beef, I'm not a bitter man. I take life as it comes. I forgive and forget. But I tell you in all seriousness, if you had heard some of the things I heard that evening –'

I swayed on my stool. 'Another time, if you don't mind, Roger. Save it for one of those long evenings before Christmas. All I want to know is which book's going to win. You heard all the discussions. You know all the ins and outs. Which is it going to be?'

'Difficult. Beef, very difficult. It won't be *Janus* apparently because it's derivative – that's the word Sabina kept using

196

which drove me mad – and it won't be *Vale of Tears* because the author's won it before and there's some sort of taboo about that. Of the other four, you can take your pick.'

'*Mandy's War* sounds a possible. A young girl's heroism during the Blitz?'

He gave me an odd look. 'It's about an art dealer.'

'What?'

'An art dealer in Florence in the 1920s. There's no Mandy and there's no war.'

'So how –'

'I told you, Beef, you haven't lived. It's a foreign country out there. The hero of *The Imbroglio* is a historian. The hero of *A Fashionable Host* is a poet. He wears old-fashioned clothes and hasn't given a party in his life. As for *The Second Coming of Franz von Hauser* –'

'Another writer?'

'A picture restorer. He's been impotent all his life, so I don't know what the first coming was. Look, I've got it with me. I'll show you.'

He dipped into his briefcase and pulled out a slim black volume with the title embossed in gold lettering.

'Just listen to some of these words, Beef. Transmogrified. Gouache. Plangent. *Condottieri*. Hermeneutic. Yang. Bibulous. Gouache again. Its called magical realism apparently.'

'What's that when it's at home?'

'A mixture of real and imaginary descriptions.'

'Like the tabloids basically?'

'More or less. Julian said it was the best book he'd read in years. Can you believe it?'

'So a likely winner?'

'Not necessarily. Jasmin hated it. Her favourite was *Vale of Tears*, although she enjoyed *The Imbroglio*. Sabina was crazy about *Mandy's War*, enjoyed *The Imbroglio*, thought *Vale of Tears* was a turkey. Quentin made a balls-aching five-minute speech about the subtle pleasures of *A Fashionable Host*, slagged off *Mandy's War*, enjoyed *The Imbroglio* in places, didn't think –'

'There's your winner then.'

'How do you mean?'

'*The Imbroglio*. It's nobody's favourite, but they all enjoyed it, so it's a natural consensus choice. All you have to do at the final selection meeting is do your Buddha bit, wait till they've torn each other to ribbons over the other ones, then say: "How about *The Imbroglio*, guys? Not a world-beater, but a damn good read. I beg to move."'

He thought about this.

'I believe you're right, Beef. I do believe you are. Nobody had a bad word to say for it and, if I know anything about committee meetings, that's going to be decisive. Take it as read, Beef. *The Imbroglio* it will be.'

'Now all we have to do is fix the odds.'

'What?'

'Gratifying though it certainly is to know the winner of a six-horse race a month in advance, it's doubly gratifying if the winner's an outsider: 16–1 for preference.'

'What are you suggesting, Beef?' he whispered, with a furtive look over his shoulder. Betting has this effect on the most robust constitutions, I don't know why.

'Rubbish *The Imbroglio* beforehand. As soon as the short list's announced, you'll get all sorts of people asking you which one you think's going to win. Some journalists, some serious people. You won't be able to say anything on the record, of course, but if you just tip the wink that the one book which doesn't have the earthly is the one with the Italian title, that should do the trick. Don't go mad. Just say the book only made the short list because the author slept with two of the judges – Quentin and Sabina, say – but its literary merits are zilch. Or say it's derivative. I don't know what the word means, but it seems to be the literary equivalent of a bruised fetlock. It should go out in the betting nicely.'

He thought about all this and gave a nervous smile. 'I could do, couldn't I, Beef?'

'Of course you could. You're not a Minister, you don't have to be squeaky-clean any more. Welcome to the real world, Roger.'

'Thanks, Beef. Another drink?'
'Absolutely.'

The next day one of the heavyweight dailies ran a story about the prize which had me purring like a kitten. Politicians may not know which way up to hold a novel but, when it comes to spreading disinformation, they leave publishers in the starting-stalls.

'The only unexpected name on the list,' ran the final paragraph, 'is Simon Harper's *The Imbroglio*. A work of no obvious literary merit, it seems to have been included on the strength of the author's personal ties with one of the judges. "Derivative from first to last," commented one well-placed insider. "It doesn't have a shout."'

The day after that came even better news. Ladbroke's made *Janus* and *A Fashionable Host* 5–2 joint favourites and offered 20–1 on *The Imbroglio*. I needed no further encouragement. Stopping only to do the necessary at my bank and pick up some travel brochures, I made a bee-line for my favourite bookmaker.

'Lovely morning, Arthur,' I said, with that ringing confidence in my voice they had learnt to dread. '*The Imbroglio* please. At 20–1.'

He scratched his ear. 'You've got me there, Mr W. Which race is it? There's the Impostor running at Hexham at three forty-five.'

'Not impostor. Imbroglio. The G is mute, which is why you didn't hear it.'

'You haven't started doing the dogs, have you, Mr W?'

'I never do the dogs. You can't trust a dog to concentrate once it realises the rabbit is a fake. This one's a book.'

'A book?'

'A book, Arthur. It's coming under starter's orders on October 15th at the Savoy Hotel. For the Damascus Prize. Ring any bells yet?'

'Sorry, Mr W, you've got me. Harry!' The shop manager came out of the back room, where he'd been counting his winnings. The third most dangerous man in London and

I'm not sure, for sheer unpleasantness, I wouldn't rank him second. 'Know anything about the Damascus Prize? Mr Wellington wants to put some money on a book.'

Harry's nose twitched. 'Which book?'

'*The Imbroglio*,' I repeated sweetly. 'For the Damascus Prize on October 15th. You're offering 20−1. It says so in black and white in the *Sporting Life*. A paper of record,' I added, underlining the point.

He shrugged and checked it on his computer. 'Give him 20−1, Arthur. How much are you putting on, Mr Wellington?'

'Five hundred please, Harry.' I took out a grubby wad from my hip-pocket. 'I'll pay tax on the stake.'

He whistled. 'Jesus, that's half a grand. We'll have to pay out ten thou if you collect. You don't normally bet more than fifty.'

'Horses are unpredictable, Harry. Books are something else.'

He shot me a suspicious look. 'You know something, don't you?'

'I know a good book when I read one. If the going's good to firm, this one will romp it. Pure pedigree. On top of which, the MCC are touring the West Indies next winter.'

'What's that got to do with it?'

'I intend to watch the Barbados match as an observer. My winnings will pay for the trip.'

'Whose winnings?'

'Mine, Harry. Your losings. It's a racing certainty.'

The prize-giving dinner at the Savoy was a black tie affair. I'd cheerfully have given it a miss – I bought my dinner-jacket when I was nineteen stone, so it's agony – but it's one of the supreme pleasures in life to watch your horse pass the winning-post in style, so I cadged an invite through Roger. There was one of those formal seating plans which do so much to spoil a good night out and I found myself billeted on table fifteen sandwiched, if that's the word, between an undernourished man of nervous disposition and a woman with a cleavage and a carrying voice. The woman took one look at me and turned her face to Mecca and the man had a problem with small-talk – he didn't have any. I raised in quick succession the subjects of horse-racing, stud poker and Oldham Athletic's chances of promotion to the first division – covered the waterfront, you might say – and all he could manage was a series of grunts. The arrival of a consommé with a single crouton in it did nothing for the general bonhomie. When the wine-waiter developed tennis elbow and started pouring the stuff as if he was footing the bill himself, I have to report that the spirits sagged. Boiled Beef, in a word.

'Are you part of the literary scene?' I asked the grunter, making one final effort.

'You c-could say that.'

'What, poems? Plays?' A sliver of fish on a bed of leeks was served and I paused to demolish it. 'Biographies?'

'Novels.'

'Novels, eh? I've heard of them, I'm not sure if I've read any. This bash must be right up your street. Ever been short-listed for the Damascus yourself?'

'Yes. In f-fact, I'm on the short list this year.'

'You don't say? Which one? *Janus*?'

'*The Second Coming –*'

'My dear friend,' I said, shaking him by the hand, 'this is a great honour. I haven't read your stuff, but you're obviously one of the stars of the show. It's a privilege to break bread with you – or it would be if they'd got around to providing any in this underfunded soup-kitchen. All your friends and relations up for the big night?'

'No, I'm on my own. That's my p-publisher if you're interested.' He pointed out a gaudily dressed woman on the other side of the table. 'I could introduce you.'

'Not now if you don't mind, Matthew.' I ingested a quail and a couple of cherries. 'It is Matthew, isn't it?'

'Yes.'

'I say, Matt, you couldn't just reach across and nobble

that spare bottle of Chardonnay, could you? There's a good man.'

I drank deep and the world suddenly seemed a whole lot sweeter. It's often the way with Chardonnay. I even found myself taking a liking to Matthew. Draw a veil over where he got his ideas from and he was just a nice, quiet, shy boy shitless with terror at being thrust into the limelight. I poured him some wine, but he didn't touch it. Nerves, you see. He was thinking he might have to make an acceptance speech and the prospect appalled him, quite understandably. I've seen this with politicians. I've seen it with bridegrooms. They get in a frightful state in what you might call the pre-speech phase and their life hangs by a thread. The sooner they're put out of their misery, the better.

Humanity was called for. I resolved to do the decent thing.

'Don't bother laying off the booze,' I said gently, as a sorbet of sorts slipped down. 'One of the others will scoop the pool and you'll have wasted an evening in needless abstinence. Have a gargle. It will do you good.'

'I won't, thank you very much. I'm not expecting to win, but just in case —'

I put my hand on his arm. 'Matt, I'm sorry because I like you, but you'd better know now. You're not going to win.'

'Are you sure?'

'Positive. It's in the bag for *The Imbroglio* and that's all there is to it.'

'How — how do you know?'

I've never seen a man so crestfallen. It was like the time old Dick Harris thought he was going to be Foreign Secretary and ended up getting No 2 at the Ministry of Ag and Fish.

'Inside knowledge,' I said with a wink. 'I don't understand the ins and outs of it, but I do know the result. *The Imbroglio* first, the rest nowhere. A procession. Yours, I think, failed to satisfy the judges because it was derivative.'

'Derivative?' he spluttered. 'But it's a highly original work.'

'Not derivative? I'll take your word for it, Matt. You wrote the thing. Too long perhaps? Too short? I'm not absolutely certain how you ploughed it, to be honest, but perhaps if, when you next put pen to paper, you try to remember –'

My foray into literary criticism was interrupted by a toastmaster calling for silence and, before I could elaborate on my ideas, Roger and the other judges were being shepherded on to the dais from the small ante-room where they had been dining on their own. The reason for this, apparently, is that literary types can't keep their mouths shut from one minute to the next and, if the judges were allowed to mingle with the general company, the cat would be out of the bag in no time and the whole thing flop as a spectator sport. Hard on poor Roger, of course, wining and dining with that shower, but it suited me fine. When you've got the inside gen yourself, you don't want everyone else muscling in – it's the first law of betting.

I've seen Roger look peakier. In fact, I've seen survivors of shipwrecks look peakier. There was a ghastly pallor in his face as if he'd suffered beyond the common lot of man. Perhaps he'd been right about Fate catching up with him. I mean, there he was, a Privy Counsellor, a former Chancellor of the Exchequer, one of the first citizens of the land, a life of blameless distinction in the public service – and the moment he hits three score years and ten, he gets put through the mangle like this. Brutal.

Some panjandrum from the Damascus Foundation introduced him and he stepped forward to the microphone with a white envelope in his hand. The television cameras zoomed in on his face. There was an expectant pause.

'Mr Chairman. Ladies and gentlemen. It's a great pleasure for me to be invited to chair the panel of judges for this distinguished prize. I don't intend to make a long speech and you won't want me to. All the books on the short list have had ardent supporters among the judges and we've had some lively discussions between ourselves. Eventually a consensus emerged. The winner of this year's Damascus Prize . . .'

He paused to open the envelope and I puffed happily at my cigar. I could practically feel the Barbados sun on my back and see the England openers going out to face the West Indies quickies.

'. . . Matthew le Fanu for *The Second Coming of Franz von Hauser*.'

The cigar fell from my lips. Matthew got to his feet and, to thunderous applause on all sides, walked up to collect his cheque. Then the whole world went dark.

Reviewing this little cock-up with Roger later, it was hard to keep the bitterness out of my voice.

'I don't mind the five hundred quid, Roger. Those were out-of-pocket expenses and the paper will stump up. Nor does kissing goodbye to ten grand mean the end of my natural life. These things happen. But I had set my heart on watching that Barbados match. It meant a lot to me.'

'I know, Beef. I'm sorry.'

'Call yourself a chairman! You couldn't chair a parish council meeting. You couldn't get a committee of bishops to pass a motion of support of Jesus. We had a foolproof plan and you blew it. Explain yourself, you pillock.'

'There's nothing to explain, Beef. It all started out exactly as we thought. They fought like cats over the other five books and couldn't agree about anything. I laid low, biding my time. Then there was a pause in the hostilities and I did my stuff. You couldn't fault me, Beef. I was diplomacy itself. I said: "Listen, everyone. We've had a long discussion and we're getting nowhere. I move we give the prize to *The Imbroglio*. You all enjoyed it. None of you have made any adverse comments about it. It seems to me the perfect compromise choice."'

'Spoken like a trooper, Roger. I've maligned you. What did they say?'

His voice dropped to a horrified whisper. 'Beef, they

crucified me. It was worse than the time I put 2p on income tax. Far worse. Quentin said my attitude was deplorable. Jasmin said a book's literary merits had nothing to do with whether anyone enjoyed it. Julian got hot under the collar and said the next thing you knew, Barbara Cartland would win the prize. As for Sabina —'

'The one you nearly hit? I can't wait.'

'She said I was a vulgar, illiterate, mid-Atlantic Philistine and I should shut up.'

'Mid-Atlantic? She's got me there. What did you do? Thump her?'

'I shut up. I'm sorry, Beef, I just lost heart. It was the sheer savagery of it all . . .' He sucked sadly at his pipe. 'You know the rest. Having ganged up on me, they buried their differences in no time and voted 4–0 for the other book. What could I do?'

We sat together in silence. The thought of that old lion being put through this sort of thing brought tears to my eyes.

'You know the final irony?' I said bitterly. 'The man who won the £20,000 jackpot won't have a clue how to spend it. I was sitting next to him. Perfectly nice, perfectly pleasant. But no social life and no interests of any sort outside his writing. A complete waste.'

Roger gave a strange smile. 'You didn't hear his acceptance speech?'

'I did not. I was sick as a parrot. I headed straight to the gents to throw up.'

'Just as well. You'd have had a nasty shock, Beef. He's a cricket fan.'

'What, that noodle?'

'He's spending the money on a trip to Barbados next winter.'

I tottered and stayed tottered.

DEREK NIMMO

TABLE TALK

Presented with the very private parts of a curried goat in Nigeria, suffering childhood picnics on the sleet-swept Pennine moors, escaping, half-starved from a health farm to gorge on a butter-oozing, calorie uncontrolled feast, recalling the wise and witty sayings of the great chefs, hosts, gourmets and gannets of the past: Derek Nimmo's *Table Talk* is a delicious, bubbling bouillabaisse of strange ingredients and unusual anecdotes.

After-dinner stories and under-the-table revelations, recipes for disaster and menus for merriment, from Victorian blowouts to the mean, lean cuisine of today: with Derek Nimmo at your elbow, you're never more than a soup-spill away from catastrophe and farce . . .

HODDER AND STOUGHTON PAPERBACKS

WOODY ALLEN

SIDE EFFECTS

'Warning: this book can harm your health. It can induce the kind of laughter that hurts and sometimes interrupts the breathing.'

Oxford Times

Worried?
Frantic?
Balding?
Reach for *Side Effects*.

For trying, middle-of-the-night anguish. When life is passing you by. Or conspiring against you. Or both. You need *Side Effects*. When you know that no one loves you and never will. When the cat has eaten your Valium and the doctor's answerphone just laughs at you. Take *Side Effects* and dissolve slowly into helpless hysteria.

HODDER AND STOUGHTON PAPERBACKS

MAX DAVIDSON

THE GREEK INTERPRETER

Half-Greek, half-German, Indian-born, Italian step-fathered Swiss-dwelling and Irish-wifed: Stavros de Battista was fated to be an interpreter.

Which was why, on the occasion of the 57th Conference of the World League of Parliaments in the Europa Hotel, Bangkok, he was drinking and thinking of fellow interpreter Christine and a spot of Addis Ababa – named after their first spasm of passion at the 1986 Plenary of the Pan-African Convention on Population Control.

Which was why he picked up the wrong pass and briefcase in the multi-lingual confusion of the accreditation desk.

Which was when life began to spiral down into a bizarre sequence of massage parlour mishaps, mistaken identities and murderous encounters . . .

'A banana-skin count high enough to content the most demanding Tom Sharpe junkie'
The Times Literary Supplement

'Hilarious' *Oxford Times*

HODDER AND STOUGHTON PAPERBACKS